Maureen J. Carter

MAGIC, MONSTERS AND ORACLES
FROM THE GREEK MYTHS

EFSTATHIADIS GROUP

*Grateful thanks to good friend and photographer Jim Iles
for the work on the illustrations
and to the Royal Botanic Gardens, Kew, London,
who very kindly provided me with the information on myrrh.*

*"Our life is frittered away by detail....
Simplify, simplify."*

Henry David Thoreau 1817-1862

Efstathiadis Group S.A.
Agiou Athanasiou Street,
GR-145 65 Anixi, Attikis

ISBN 960 226 554 X

© Efstathiadis Group S.A. 1996

Printed and bound in Greece by Efstathiadis Group S.A.

To my mother.

Contents

Part 3 Oracles

Part 1
MAGIC

INTRODUCTION

The ancient Greek people, from about 3500 BC, worshipped a number of gods who, they said, came from Gaia, Mother Earth, and Chaos, the beginning of all things. For a while, these Gods were ruled by Cronus, son of Gaia, but even amongst these immortal and powerful gods things were not well and eventually Cronus was overthrown by his son, Zeus.

Zeus came to govern all the Gods from his throne on Mount Olympus, aided by eleven members of his immediate family. The ancient Greeks attributed to him and his fellow Gods all of the virtues and many of the vices of their own human nature . So all the Gods were capable not only of love and laughter, of kindness and caring, but also of jealousy and greed, of cruelty and teasing. They were very powerful deities. Zeus could kill with a thunderbolt and disguise himself to seduce beautiful nymphs and even humans. Nymphs were semi-divine creatures of nature who inhabited the woods and rivers. Zeus and some of the other Gods could not resist them.

All the Gods were capable of travelling vast distances in fractions of a second and, like Zeus, they could change their form at will. Not only that, they could all transform human beings into animals, birds, trees and flowers or even into rivers and springs. The following tales are of those magical transformations when the Gods, either as a punishment that fitted the crime, or as an act of benevolence, turned people and nymphs into something other than their original form.

You will, of course, meet most of the gods in the stories in this section and the sections that follow. To help you, here is a list of those gods in alphabetical order, together with a little information on each of them. The star denotes one of the twelve Olympian gods.

APHRODITE *
The beautiful goddess of love, born from the foam of the sea.

APOLLO *
A son of Zeus and twin brother of Artemis. He and his sister were called the Heavenly Twins. His mother was Leto and he was the god of music and archery. He was also a healer and a prophet.

ARES *
God of war and the son of Zeus and Hera. Wherever he went, Fear and Panic went with him.

ARTEMIS *
Twin sister of Apollo, she was the goddess of hunting and the guardian of wild animals.

ATHENA *
A daughter of Zeus, she was the goddess of arts and crafts and also the goddess of war. She became guardian of the city of Athens.

DEMETER *
Goddess of fertility, as a sister of Zeus she should have been one of the twelve ruling gods of Olympus, but she preferred to remain on earth, caring for the crops in the fields.

DIONYSUS
The god of wine and vegetation. Those who worshipped him were often drunk.

EOS
She was the goddess of the dawn and her children were the four winds.

EROS
The god of love. His golden tipped arrows filled people with love but he could also shoot lead tipped arrows, full of hate.

GAIA
Mother Earth; from her, by Chaos, in the presence of love or Eros, came all living things.

HADES *
Powerful god of the Underworld. He did not often leave his nether regions.

HELIUS
The sun god, who drove his golden chariot each day, from east to west, across the sky. As he drove, he saw all things from his position high above the earth.

HEPHAESTUS *
The god of fire, volcanoes and metalwork. His forge was underneath Mount Etna where, amongst other things, he fashioned golden chariots for the gods.

HERA *
Wife of Zeus. She was the

goddess of women and marriage and the chief goddess of childbirth. Her own marriage was not too happy, for Zeus was always chasing other goddesses and nymphs and making her very jealous.

HERMES *

The messenger of the gods and helper of travellers. He was also a musician and invented the lyre, making it out of the shell of a tortoise, with sheep gut for its seven strings.

HESTIA *

Does not figure in these tales but she was the sister of Zeus, one of the twelve Olympian gods and was goddess of the hearth. Every city had a public hearth built to honour Hestia, where a flame burned continuously.

IRIS

The rainbow goddess and another messenger of the gods.

LETO

A daughter of the night, an ancient goddess and mother of the Heavenly Twins, Apollo and Artemis.

MUSES

These were nine daughters of Zeus who were the goddesses of the arts; of music, poetry and memory.

PAN

He was a shepherd god, half goat, who lived in the mountains and woods of Arcadia.

PENEUS

This was a river god. Nearly all the river gods were sons of the greatest river god, Oceanus, who flowed in a great circle around the earth.

PERSEPHONE

Daughter of Demeter, she became goddess of the underworld when Hades kidnapped her. But she only stayed with Hades for four months each year and during that time, nothing grew on earth. These were the winter months.

PONTUS

Child of Gaia, father of the sea god Nereus.

POSEIDON *

The god of the Seas. He was also god of horses and earthquakes.

RHEA

Wife of Cronus and mother of the goddess of fertility, Demeter.

URANUS

The sky. He mated with his

mother, Gaia, to become father of the Titans, including Cronus, the Hecatoncheires and the Cyclopes.

ZEPHYRUS
God of the west wind.

ZEUS *
All powerful ruler of the Heavens and the Universe from his kingdom on Mount Olympus. He was married to Hera but had many love affairs with other goddesses, nymphs and even humans.

Hyacinthus Orientalis

HYACINTH

There lived a young prince, in Sparta, called Hyacinthus, a beautiful youth, with whom the God Apollo fell in love. It is said that his love for the boy was so strong that he no longer played his music or hunted with his bow and even that he neglected to proclaim the Oracle at Delphi, preferring to remain with Hyacinthus in Sparta. Unfortunately, Zephyrus, the West Wind, also took a fancy to the boy.

One lovely summer's day, out on the Spartan plains, Apollo was giving Hyacinthus, who had become his constant companion, a lesson in discus throwing. As they competed for the longest throw, out of the west came the jealous Zephyrus, snatching the discus in mid-air with a sudden gust of wind, hurling it at the young prince's head.

The boy fell to the ground, fatally wounded. Apollo cradled him in his arms, vainly trying to staunch the flow of blood as it spilled out, mingled with the god's tears and dyed the grass red. In his grief Apollo called out "alas, alas." Where the blood fell on the grass, a beautiful crimson flower sprang up. Apollo marked it "Ai", Greek for "alas" and called it the hyacinth. In this way, the god immortalised the boy as, each spring, on the hillsides of Greece, the sweetly scented hyacinth orientalis appears, although the flower must have evolved over the years and the sign faded, as our hyacinth today bears no such letters.

Games, known as the Hyacinthean Games, were held each year in remembrance of the boy.

A CICADA

A young prince, Tithonus, was taken from his father's palace by the Goddess of the Dawn, Eos, who had fallen for the handsome youth. The pair lived happily in Ethiopia where, very much in love, Eos begged Zeus to grant immortality to Tithonus. However, she forgot to ask the great god to grant the boy eternal youth, to go hand in hand with the gift of everlasting life. So, over the years, her lover aged. His hair turned gray. His skin wrinkled. His body bent and his voice became hoarse but he could not die. As the years went relentlessly on, Tithonus shrivelled. He became so feeble and ugly that Eos could not bear to look at him and she shut him up in a room, alone. But In the end she took pity on the dried up, withered creature that he had become. The only thing left of him was his hoarse, strident voice, so she turned him into a cicada, that shrill-voiced, transparent winged insect which

11

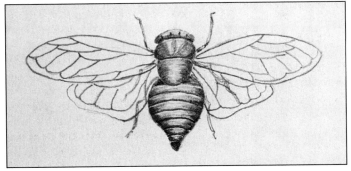

Cicada

sings all through the hot Mediterranean summer, yet is rarely seen.

THE LAUREL TREE

Apollo boasted one day, to Eros, God of Love, of his superior bowmanship. The angry Eros took his revenge by preparing two arrows. The first he dipped into a potion that would fill its victim with an indifference to love. This arrow he fired at the nymph, Daphne, the lovely young daughter of the River God, Peneus. So, although she had many suitors, Daphne rejected them all and became a

Sweet Laurel

lover of the woods and countryside around her home, where she hunted. Her father despaired of ever seeing her married and knowing the joy of holding his grandchild in his arms.

Eros dipped his second arrow into a love potion and fired it at Apollo, filling the God with a desire for the lovely Daphne. But the nymph spurned the god's advances and he, unable to curb his lust for her, gave chase.

Daphne ran from the god until she could run no more. She had reached a river, where the waters of her father, Peneus, ran. She called out to him for help and, as she felt Apollo's breath on her neck, she became rooted to the ground. The god reached out for her and found himself clasping a young laurel tree.

The laurel, with its aromatic leaves, which are much used in cooking and we know as bay, still likes to grow in damp places and river beds, in Greece. The tree and all others of its kind became sacred to Apollo, all those competing in his name and winning, being crowned with laurel leaves.

A SWALLOW, A NIGHTINGALE AND A HOOPOE

Tereus, King of Thrace and son of the god Ares, was married to Procne, who asked him, one day, to fetch her sister from Athens. The king duly set sail, but when he met her, Tereus fell in love with the beautiful Philomela. He deceived her, spinning a familiar tale, telling the girl that his wife, Procne, was dead and, on the journey back to Thrace, the pair became lovers. When Philomela discovered that her sister still lived, she was horrified and threatened to reveal the truth; so Tereus cut out her tongue and shut her away. He then returned to his wife, saying that her sister had died on the voyage.

Although she could not speak, Philomela found a way to tell her story. She set to work on her loom and wove the tale, in the form of pictures, into a wonderful tapestry, which she gave to her servant to send to the Queen, her sister. On receiving the gift, Procne unrolled the cloth and, seeing the pictures, went at once to release Philomela.

On her return to the palace, Procne, full of hate for her husband, could not bear to look at the child she had born him, so she killed the boy, cut him up and fed the pieces to Tereus. When he had finished his meal, she told him what he had eaten, before fleeing with her sister. Tereus, momentarily stunned by her words, took up his sword and gave chase. He was about to kill the two women when the gods turned him and the fleeing pair into birds. Tereus became the hoopoe, his battle helmet a crest of feathers and his sword a long beak. Procne was transformed into a nightingale and, to this day, sings a sad song as she

13

A Hoopoe

remembers the terrible thing she did to her child. The nightingale bears traces of the murder on its tail feathers, tinged blood red. Philomela, contrary to popular belief, became a twittering swallow, unable to sing without her tongue.

These three birds are summer visitors to Greece. The swallow has no song; it truly only twitters. The nightingale's song is liquid and sad. The hoopoe frequents vineyards and orchards where it nests in holes.

A LIZARD

The goddess Demeter, that deity of fertility, was heartbroken when Hades, god of the Underworld, on a rare

Agami lizard

visit to the upper regions, abducted her daughter, Core. Demeter searched for her ceaselessly, taking neither food nor drink for nine days.

Wearing disguise, she arrived one day at Eleusis, where she was invited by the king, Celeus, to eat and drink. Accepting a refreshing, mint-flavoured draught, the weary Demeter quaffed it thirstily, only to be criticised by Celeus' son, Abas, for being greedy.

The usually gentle goddess, probably at the end of her tether, turned to the boy with a withering look and, in an instant, he became a lizard, a reptile whose whole make up is given over to conserving water.

AN OWL

Demeter continued her search for Core, refusing to allow the crops to grow on earth until, in desperation at the plight of mankind, Zeus asked Hades to release the girl. Hades said that, as long as she did not eat any food from the Underworld, he would let her go. Just as Core was leaving, however, a gardener of those nether regions, a certain Ascelaphus, reported that he had seen the girl eat seven

Short eared owl

pomegranate seeds. With mankind on the brink of starvation, Zeus persuaded Demeter and Hades to compromise. Core would stay in Hades for three months of each year, returning in the spring to her mother. Demeter punished Ascelaphus for his tale-telling by turning him into a short eared owl.

This bird visits Greece in the winter, the time when Core is with Hades in the Underworld. It can often be seen by day, flying over open grassland and rough hillsides.

A BEAR

Zeus fell in love with Callisto, the daughter of a king of Arcadia. He saw her in the woods one day, alone, and appeared to her disguised as Artemis, goddess of Hunting. As they talked, he stroked the girl and eventually embraced her. Callisto saw through the disguise at once but the god was too strong and had his way with her. Some time later, when Callisto was bathing naked in a pool, Hera, wife of Zeus, noticed her pregnancy and realised what had happened. The girl bore Zeus

Brown bear

a son, Arcas, but as soon as the birth was over, the angry Hera turned Callisto into a bear.

For fifteen years Callisto lived in the shape of a bear, in the woods of Arcadia, until the day when Hera contrived that Arcas, out hunting, would kill the she-bear. But the situation was saved by Zeus, who took Callisto and put her in the heavens, where we know her as the Great Bear. On his death, Arcas joined his mother in the sky as the Little Bear.

Brown bears used to roam the forests of Greece but are now confined to the very north of the country. They are solitary creatures and their diet is usually vegetarian.

REEDS, THE PAN PIPES AND THE EARS OF AN ASS

The god Pan was born in Arcadia, where he frequented the woods, mountains and high places. He had the horns, ears and feet of a goat but, though a great romantic by nature, he was usually unsuccessful in love, owing to his ugliness.

One day, he fell in love with a young nymph, named Syrinx, chasing the poor maiden far and wide. At last he caught up with her and grabbed her, only to find

The giant reed

that her sister nymphs had changed her into a reed. Pan heaved a great sigh and the breath of his sigh blew through the reed, producing a lovely sound.

Pan, a musician, hacked down the reed, cut it into pieces and made himself a musical instrument, called the pan pipes or syrinx to this day.

Once he had mastered his new instrument, Pan became so proud of himself that he had the audacity to say that he was better on his pipes than Apollo was on his lyre. A contest was held and Apollo won. But it so happened that one of the judges, King Midas, had been foolish enough to cast his vote for Pan. Apollo gave him the ears of an ass, a fitting punishment, he thought, for one with such bad hearing. Midas was so ashamed of the ears that he kept them under a hat but, of course, when he had his hair cut his barber had to see them. Now that barber swore to keep the king's affliction a secret, but soon he could no longer bear to keep it to himself. So he dug a hole in the ground, spoke the secret into it and covered it up. Reeds grew where the hole had been and, when the wind blew, they whispered the story of the king's ears on the breeze.

The giant reed grows in Greece, in damp places, where it resembles bamboo and is used for making fishing rods, walking sticks and for screening purposes.

THE PINE TREE

Pan fell in love with Pitys, a nymph of the pine trees, but she did not respond to his advances, probably owing to the usual problem, Pan's goat-like features. Like Syrinx, she had to flee from his advances and was turned into a pine tree before the god could reach her. Pan took a branch from the tree and made it into a wreath which, from that moment, he always wore on his head.

The pine remains sacred to Pan. The Aleppo pine is tapped for its resin which flavours and preserves the wine, retsina. Pine wood was used in ancient Greece for ship building.

The Aleppo pine

WOLVES.....

Callisto's father, King Lycaeon of Arcadia, had fifty sons. Some say that he was wicked, but others hold that he was responsible for introducing the worship of the great god, Zeus, into Arcadia. He made the mistake, though, of sacrificing a child to the god and the angry Zeus, finding such an offering unacceptable, turned Lycaeon into a wolf.

However, the fifty sons of the king really were wicked and Zeus decided to pay them a visit. He

Wolf

went in disguise and they served him their brother, Nyctimus, chopped up in a soup. The horrified god turned them all into wolves and gave Nyctimus back his life. In his disgust at the wickedness of mankind, the god sent a great deluge of rain to flood the earth.

It is said that the top of Mount Parnassus remained above water and the citizens of the city of Parnassus were woken by the howling of wolves. They followed the pack up the mountain and so survived the flood.

The wolf is no longer to be found in Greece, but its smaller cousin, the jackal, ranges all over the area.

... AND WOLVERINES

When the flood waters receded, those people from Parnassus went to live in Arcadia where they began to make human sacrifices once more. The offal from the victim's body was put into a soup and lots were drawn by the local shepherds, for the helping which contained these innards. Legend had it that the shepherd who ate these, became a wolverine. If he then refrained from eating human flesh for eight years, he regained his human form.

Wolverine

The wolverine is a greedy scavenger and is a member, the largest, of the weasel family.

A HEIFER

Zeus fell in love again. This time with the lovely Io, daughter of Inachus of Argos, but to protect himself and his new love from the wrath of the jealous Hera, he caused a cloud to hang over the earth, which hid them. Hera, however, guessed why the great blanket of fog had appeared and made it evaporate. Zeus immediately turned Io into a white heifer, just in time, for Hera found the two standing together and once again,

knowing the god's nature, guessed what had happened. She commented on the beauty of the cow and asked if she could have it as a gift. Zeus could not refuse and Hera put Io under the one hundred watchful eyes of Argus, the guardian of her herds. King Inachus wept so many tears at the loss of his daughter that the river Anachus was formed, the principal river of Argos.

Zeus sent Hermes to kill Argus. That god, playing the pan pipes, told Argus the story of Pan, Syrinx and the pipes. For some reason, the tale and the music lulled the guard into sleep and his one hundred eyes closed.

Hermes slew him and set Io free.

Hera, in her anger, sent a horse fly to torture Io, who was still in the form of a white heifer. In agony, she ran here and there, at one time *The Peacock* jumping into the sea in an unsuccessful attempt to shake off the maddening insect. The waters were known ever after as the Ionian Sea. Io continued to travel the land, trying to escape the horsefly, eventually finding herself in Egypt. There, Zeus restored her to human shape, she bore him a son and lived happily until her death. One of the descendants, from the love of Io and Zeus, was that great hero, Heracles.

Hera found a way to honour her herdsman, Argus. She placed his one hundred eyes in the tail of her favourite bird, the peacock.

MINT

Hades, the god of the Under-world, sometimes called the Unseen One, rarely emerged from his underground kingdom. One day, however, on a visit to the upper world, he caught sight of Menthe, a beautiful nymph, and was filled with desire for her. He approached her, driving his shining golden chariot, pulled by jet black horses. Menthe, dazzled by the sight, would have gone to him but before she could move, the queen of the Underworld, Persephone, turned her into a fragrant plant, the green and perennial mint.

Apple mint, or menthe suaveolens, can be found

Mint

growing wild in Greece. It seldom produces flowers but has a minty, apple smell.

A SPIDER

Arachne was a weaver, no ordinary weaver, but the most skilful in Lydia. Unfortunately, she was not very

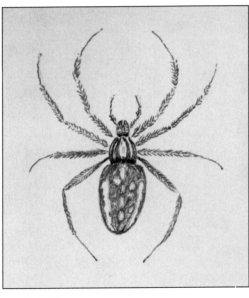

A garden spider

modest, boasting that she was better than the mighty Athena herself, even challenging the goddess to a contest. Athena agreed and the two women set

to work, each weaving a marvellous piece of cloth.

Arachne wove pictures of the love affairs of the gods into her work and the angry Athena could find no fault in it. In a rage, she tore the cloth to bits and the terrified Arachne hung herself from the ceiling. As she hung from the beams, the goddess turned her into a spider, condemning her to weave her silken webs for the rest of her life.

The common garden spider spins its web from silk glands in the abdomen. When it catches its prey in the resultant mesh, it injects it with poison from its fangs.

A PARTRIDGE

Daedalus was a famous Athenian craftsman and inventor. One of his apprentices, however, a certain Talos, surpassed his master, inventing the saw and the potter's wheel among other things.

Daedalus was jealous of course, but Talos put the final nail in his own coffin when he seduced Polycaste, his own mother. His horrified master took him up to the Acropolis, under the pretext of showing him

The rock partridge

the view, and pushed him over the edge. Polycaste hung herself when she heard of his death, but some god must have felt sympathy for Talos, as he was turned into a partridge before he could finish his fall.

The rock partridge breeds all over Greece, enjoying the stony ground and the vineyards.

THE OAK AND THE LINDEN TREE

One day, the gods Zeus and Hermes were wandering the earth, disguised as mortals. They arrived at a town but were not welcomed there, so they made their way up the mountain that towered behind the town and came upon a poor hut, belonging to an elderly couple, Philemon and Baucis.

With typical Greek hospitality, the old people offered what little they had to the two strangers, making a meal out of almost nothing, bustling about, making their guests comfortable. Philemon took a jug, filled it with the last of his wine and poured it for them. While they talked of this and that, Philomen noticed that the wine jug kept filling itself. The old couple grew very frightened when they realised that they were entertaining, not ordinary people, but gods. Zeus and Hermes, however, took the pair outside their hut and told them to look down into the valley below. The town that had refused to offer hospitality to the gods had vanished under a lake. When the couple turned to go

23

Kermes oak

probably the kermes oak, an evergreen tree with prickly, holly-like leaves, its yellow catkins appearing in the spring, with the young leaves.

A STAG

Actaeon was a mortal, a great hunter. Perhaps stories of his prowess offended the goddess of Hunting, Artemis, because, out with his hounds one day, hot and tired from the hunt, he came to a lake. There he discovered Artemis bathing. To prevent him from boasting to his friends that he had seen her nakedness, the goddess turned him into a stag, making no attempt to interfere

The stag

back into their hut, it had been transformed into a magnificent temple.

The two gods said they would grant the couple whatever they wished. They wanted only to guard the temple and, in life and death, never to part. The gods granted the wishes. The pair became the guardians of the temple until they reached a good old age. One day, as they stood together, they found that they could not move. Their skin became bark, two trees grew as one, putting out the leaves of the linden and the oak, grafted together for all time.

The linden tree is the lime, whose fragrant, yellow/white flowers can be toxic to bees. The oak was

when his own dogs turned on him and tore him to pieces.

24

The unhappy dogs, grieving at the loss of their master, sat and howled until Cheiron, the centaur, took pity on them and made a statue of Actaeon for them.

The stag was probably the male of the red deer, now only found in Central Greece. It is the largest deer in most of Europe.

KINGFISHERS

Alcyone was the daughter of Aeolus, king of the Winds. She married Ceyx, a king of Thessaly, son of the Morning Star. The two were deeply in love. One day Ceyx, weighed down by affairs of state, decided to go to Delphi to consult the Oracle about his worries. Alcyone implored him not to go on the dangerous journey, saying she knew about the winds and what they could do to ships in their wilder moments. Ceyx was adamant and set off, regardless of his wife's pleas.
His ship was wrecked before he had gone very far and his body washed up near the headland where Alcyone stood, watching for him. In her grief, seeing her dead husband, she jumped into the sea, intending to drown herself, but found that she was flying above the surface of the water. The gods had taken pity on her and turned her into a kingfisher. Beside her flew her husband, who had been turned into the same bird. Each year, at the winter solstice, the pair nested on the sea for seven days, while the waters remained calm for them. The Halcyon days.

The kingfisher is at home in Greece, where this brilliantly coloured bird will not only be found near fresh water, but also in coastal estuaries.

25

The kingfisher

MYRRH and......

A certain king, Cinyras, had a beautiful daughter, Smyrna. So lovely was she that he boasted that she out dazzled Aphrodite. The insulted goddess caused Smyrna to fall in love with her own father.

So, although suitors came to ask for her hand from far and wide, Smyrna refused them all until, tortured by her terrible love, she tried to kill herself. Her nurse found her just in time and, when she discovered the poor girl's torment, decided to help her. One night, when Cinyras had taken too much wine and lay in a drunken stupor, the nurse let Smyrna into her father's room and, in the dark and without knowing it, the father took his own daughter. When, some time later, it became obvious that his daughter was pregnant and a horrified Cinyras discovered the truth, that he was the father of the child, he threw her out of the palace.

Once over the shock, Cinyras seized his sword and rushed after the weeping girl but when he caught up with her, Aphrodite turned her into a myrrh tree at the moment when Cinyras was swinging his sword, ready to kill her. As the weapon descended, it split the tree in two and from the cleft the baby was born.

The myrrh tree, now only native to Ethiopia and parts of Arabia, weeps still, the drops forming a resin used in medicine and perfumery.

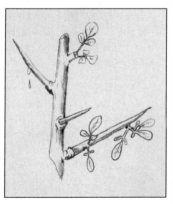

The spiny myrrh

......ANEMONES

A phrodite took the baby, born from the cloven myrrh tree, naming it Adonis. She put it in a chest, which she gave to Persephone, queen of the Underworld, to hide. With a curiosity natural to women, Persephone opened the chest and discovered the baby. She brought it up and Adonis grew into the loveliest of youths. Aphrodite, hearing of his beauty, went to the Underworld to claim him, where the two women fought over him and eventually the affair had to be judged by a court. The decision was that, each year, Persephone had the boy for four months, then he would go to Aphrodite for four months and the rest of the time was his own. Aphrodite, however, was so much taken with the boy that she cheated. She owned a magic girdle and, when she wore it, no man could resist her, especially Adonis, who stayed with her all year. Persephone went to the god Ares for help. He disguised himself as a boar and gored Adonis to death.

Aphrodite arrived too late but, seeing the ground spattered with the blood of Adonis, she sprinkled the drops with sweet nectar. Soon, where every drop had fallen, sprang a scarlet flower.

Each year, when the red anemones bloom, soon to be blown away by the March winds, we are reminded of the short life of the beautiful Adonis.

Anemone

BLUE SPOTTED SNAKES

Cadmus was the founder of the city of Thebes. When he married Harmonia, the daughter of Aphrodite and Ares, the gods of Olympus broke with tradition and attended the earthly wedding, seated on twelve golden thrones in the city market place. Apollo, it is said, provided sweet music with his lyre, Athena presented the pair with a magnificent gold robe and Aphrodite gave a necklace, fashioned by the smith god,

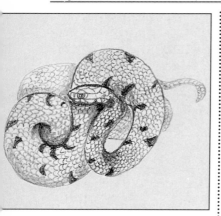

The grass snake

Hephaestus.

Now it happened that Dionysus had foretold that Cadmus and Harmonia would one day rule over barbarians, who would attack not only Greek cities, but also the very temple of Apollo. The pair would be punished for this but Ares would save them and turn them into serpents.

When Cadmus gave up the throne of Thebes, he and Harmonia left the city and retired to Illyria, whose people made him their king. As had been foretold, the war-like Illyrians attacked Apollo's temple, but were defeated. After the battle, Cadmus and Harmonia would have been killed, had not Ares

turned them into blue-spotted snakes. He sent them to live in that happy place where mortals go who have found favour with the gods; the Elysian Fields.

Snakes, both poisonous and non poisonous, can be found all over Greece and it is advisable to be cautious when walking, in the summer, through long grass and wild shrubland.

GUINEA FOWL

A certain King Oineus of Kalydon forgot to sacrifice to Artemis and, as a punishment, she sent a wild boar to ravage his land. The king's son, Meleager, gathered a group of heroes to hunt the animal down. Taking part in the hunt was a virgin huntress named Atalanta and Meleager fell in love with her, offering her the boar's pelt when the hunt was over. When his mother's brothers tried to prevent him from presenting her with the hide, he killed them.

Now it so happened that, when Meleager was born, the Fates had appeared and foretold that he would die when a brand, which was on the fire at the time,

28

was reduced to ashes. Meleager's mother, horrified, snatched the brand from the fire and locked it away for many years. But, to revenge the death of her brothers, she retrieved it. She threw it on the fire and Meleager collapsed and died. His keening, mourning sisters were turned, by Artemis, into guinea fowl.

Guinea fowl used to be widespread in North Africa so, perhaps, at the time these stories were told, they inhabited parts of Greece. They are gregarious, cackling birds which like to nest in trees.

Guinea fowl

AN ECHO AND A NARCISSUS

The great goddess, Hera, in one of the jealous rages to which she was given, was following her husband, Zeus, suspecting him of having one of his many affairs. Travelling through some woods, she came upon a group of nymphs. They were chattering gaily, in particular one of them named Echo. Hera, quite wrongly, decided that Echo was the subject of her husband's affection and dealt her a severe punishment. The lovely nymph suddenly found that she could not speak of her own accord. She could only repeat the last few words that had been said to her. So the echo was born. Now Echo fell in love with a beautiful boy, Narcissus, but could not tell him of her feelings. Unfortunately, Narcissus loved nothing and no-one. Echo followed him everywhere, repeating his words in frustration, but he would not listen. In her grief and shame, she hid herself away, in dark and cavernous places, wasting away until only her voice was left. We can still hear her today, in those

29

Narcissus "Pheasant's eye"

30

places where she likes to hide. But Narcissus did fall in love eventually. Leaning over a pool one day, he saw his own reflection and fell in love with himself. So strong was his passion for his reflected image that he could not tear himself away from the water's edge, not even for food. So he wasted away and died. When the nymphs came to bury him, they found no body, only a flower, drooping over the pool.

The flower became known as the narcissus and was often associated with death.

The pheasant's eye narcissus grows in Greece as a solitary flower, its head bent, flowering from April to June.

A WEASEL

Alcmene was married to a general, Amphitryon, who led an expedition against the Taiphians, who had murdered his wife's brothers. During his absence, Zeus lay with Alcmene and Amphitryon was placated, on his return, when he learned that the lover had been none other than the great god himself. When the time came for Alcmene's baby to be born from the seed of Zeus, the insanely jealous Hera tricked the god into announcing that any descendant of his, born before midnight that day, would rule Tiryns.

Hera rushed to that city where Nicippe, another woman loved by Zeus, had been made pregnant by him. The goddess brought about a premature birth, after she had sent Illythia, the goddess of childbirth, to Alcmene with strict instructions to retard the delivery of her child. Poor Alcmene was in labour for many hours while Illythia sat on her doorstep with legs tightly

The weasel

crossed, her way of preventing birth. When it looked as if Alcmene would die, along with her baby, one of her attendants, a woman called Galanthis, had an idea. She ran out of the room, crying happily that the baby was born. Illythia sprang to her feet in surprise, uncrossing her legs and the child was safely delivered. Although the birth had occurred after midnight and Hera's plans had not been thwarted, the angry goddess, nevertheless, turned Galanthis into a weasel.

The weasel is the smallest of the carnivores. It preys on voles and mice. A good climber, it will kill birds and steal eggs.

WHITE DOVES

A certain Anius, king of Delos, had three daughters, Elais, Spermo and Oeno, called the Wine-growers. He dedicated them to Dionysus, god of Wine, who, in return, gave each girl a gift. What Elais touched, if she called upon the god, he would turn to oil; what Spermo touched, to corn and what Oeno touched, to wine.

Dove

So it was to Anius that Agamemnon turned when he wanted to provision the Greek fleet for its expedition to Troy. The three daughters of Anius provided corn, oil and wine sufficient for the fleet, but Agamemnon decided that it would be better to take the girls themselves, as well. He sent Odysseus for them, but they escaped from him. Agamemnon gave chase by sea and they surrendered to him, but called upon Dionysus for help. He turned them into white doves.

The snowy white dove, which has become a sign of peace, is a bird much loved on the island of Delos.

POPLAR TREES AND A SWAN

Cycnus, a musician king of Liguria, was the inseparable friend of Phaethon, son of Helius, the Sun god. Now Phaethon was brought up by Merops, an Egyptian king. When, as a young man, he found that his parentage was in question, he made the difficult journey to the edge of the world, to find Helius, where he asked him if he was his true father. Helius rashly promised

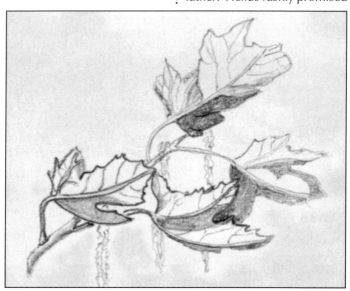

White poplar

to do anything the boy wished, to prove that this was the case. Unfortunately, Phaethon asked for the impossible. Permission to drive the great chariot of the sun across the sky for one day. Unable to refuse, Helius reluctantly handed over the reins.

The youth could not control the horses. It is said that they streaked across the sky, causing the Milky Way, before tumbling towards the earth, setting the very mountains on fire, scorching the land to form deserts and drying up rivers. Zeus, to save the situation, killed Phaethon with a thunderbolt, whereupon he fell, flaming, from the sky, his body plunging into the river Eridanus.

Phaethon's sisters wept for him, beside the river, until they were turned into poplar trees. The sisters wept on, their tears dripped down the bark, the sun hardened them and they fell as lumps of amber into the river, to be washed away to far off lands. Cycnus wandered through the poplar grove, mourning, until he was turned into a swan by Apollo and placed among the stars.

The poplar grows well in Greece, beside rivers, enjoying a moist soil and perhaps its catkins, produced in late spring, resemble drops of amber.

A RIVER AND A SPRING

Arethusa was a lovely young Nereid or sea nymph, who lived in Achaea. One day she was noticed by Alpheius, a hunter, who immediately fell in love with her. She refused his attentions and, fleeing from him, found refuge on the island of Ortygia, where she became a spring.

The gods took pity on the love sick Alpheius, who would have died of grief, and turned him into a river, the Alpheius. His waters ran into the sea as a fresh water current which flowed to Ortygia, where it reached the waters of the spring Arethusa, mingling together for all time. Legend has it that, when bulls were sacrificed near the river Alpheius on the Peloponnesus, the spring waters of Arethusa on Ortygia ran tinged with blood.

MONKEYS

The two Cercopes were mischievous little men,

The Ververt Monkey

thieves and robbers, who lived in Lydia, a region of Asia Minor. Now a certain great hero, Heracles, had been sent to Lydia as a punishment. He had to work as a slave to the queen, Omphale, who had sent him to capture the Cercopes. He succeeded in the task, tying the two men to a pole which he slung over his shoulder, before going on his way. After a while he heard the two men giggling.

It so happened that, when the two were young, their mother had warned them to keep away from a certain Blackbottom. Now Heracles' tunic was very short and the sun had burned his bottom very dark. The Cercopes, hanging upside down from the pole behind Heracles, had suddenly realised who Blackbottom was and thought the situation very amusing. Heracles set down the pole and asked to share in the joke, which he enjoyed so much that he set the two free. Unfortunately for them, they had not learned their lesson and continued with their trickery and thievery until, in the end, Zeus, the greatest of gods, turned them into monkeys.

There are no monkeys living wild in Greece today, but perhaps the vervet, a monkey which today lives in the forests of west and central Africa, once inhabited Asia Minor.

A HAWK

Daedalion had a beautiful daughter, Chione. One day as she walked in the woods near her home, she was seen by both Hermes and Apollo, who were intoxicated by her beauty.

Hawk

Hermes put her to sleep at once and lay with her. Apollo waited until night before going to her bed and seducing her.

So, some months later, the girl gave birth to two sons, both children of the gods and this feat went to her head. She boasted that she was more beautiful even than the lovely Artemis. This was too much for that huntress and she let loose an arrow at the girl, killing her. Daedalion, overcome with sorrow at the loss of his daughter, threw himself from Mount Parnassus but, before he fell to his death, Apollo turned him into a hawk.

The bird could have been a goshawk, which hunts fast and low and would have enjoyed the rich forests on the slopes of Parnassus.

INCENSE AND THE HELIOTROPE

Helius, god of the Sun, could see all things. When Aphrodite was unfaithful to her husband, Hephaestus, it was Helius who made the story public and, in revenge, the goddess filled him with desire for a mortal, Leucothea.

However, at one time, Helius

Heliotrope

36

had made love to Clytie, Leucothea's sister and the girl became jealous of the god's new love, going to tell her father, Orchamos, of the affair. Orchamos had Leucothea buried alive. Helius arrived at the scene too late to save her, although he tried to penetrate the earth with his rays to warm her body and bring it back to life, but in vain. So he turned her into the aromatic incense shrub.

Clytie realised that she had made a mistake, for she had caused Helius to hate her. She sat on the ground outside her house, gazing at her lost love. She took

neither food nor drink, wasting away, becoming one with the soil, slowly turning into a bright flower, whose purple petals followed the sun from its rising to its setting. She had become the evergreen heliotrope.

The heliotrope is a fragrant shrub, producing its purple flowers all through the summer months. It loves to grow in full sun.

MAGPIES

The nine muses, possessors of many gifts, were known as the Queens of Song. A certain King Pierus of Macedonea had nine daughters who also sang sweetly. But they grew too proud of their talent and challenged the Muses to a contest.

Magpie

The nymphs were the judges and, not unnaturally, the muses, represented by Calliope, won. They punished the boastful sisters by turning them into magpies.

These handsome birds, which do not sing, are known for their loud, hoarse chattering.

A LARK
AND
AN OSPREY

Nisus, king of Megara, had three daughters, one of them called Scylla. King Minos of Crete attacked Megara and would have failed to take the city had not Scylla fallen in love with the handsome Cretan. The girl knew that her father's life, for some reason, depended on his keeping his golden hair. So, one night, while he slept, she cut off his locks and presented them to Minos, thinking to earn his appreciation. But, horrified at her treachery, King Minos was neither grateful nor did he fall in love with her as she hoped, but had her drowned, whereupon the gods turned her into a lark. Minos succeeded in taking Megara, for it was without a king

and the gods, with some justification, turned Nisus into an osprey, that bird which preys upon smaller birds, including the lark.

Osprey

The osprey is a winter visitor to Greece. A flesh eating bird of prey with a hooked beak and powerful talons, it breeds in woodland, near lakes and rivers. The short toed lark, visiting Greece only in summer, perhaps to avoid the osprey, sings in flight, sounding a little like the willow warbler.

A SPRING OF FRESH WATER

Aking of Arcadia had a beautiful daughter, Alope. The god of the Sea, Poseidon, who had almost as many affairs as Zeus himself, seduced the girl and she bore his child in secret. She wrapped the baby in her cloak and ordered her nurse to leave it on a mountain to die. A wandering shepherd found the child and took it back to his hut, but a neighbouring shepherd quarrelled with him, not so much over the baby, but more over the rich robe in which it was wrapped. A fight ensued.

The two were taken before the king, who had to act as arbitrator in their quarrel. When he saw the robe and recognised it as his daughter's, he had her thrown in the dungeons and ordered that the child be put, once more, out on the mountain to die. A mare suckled the baby boy until the shepherds found it again and brought it up, this time in peace. The child grew to be a king of Arcadia, but the mother languished to death in the dungeon. She was buried near Eleusis and the god of the sea Poseidon, turned her into a fresh water spring.

Water is precious in Greece and where there is a good spring, some stonework protection is often provided and a trough or basin is hewn out of the rock to catch the water.

ANTS BECOME MEN

Aeacus, king of the island of Aegina, was the son of Zeus and the nymph Aegina. Hera,

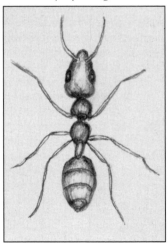

The common ant

furious at her husband's affair with the nymph, vented her wrath on the son of the union, sending a terrible plague to his island kingdom. Aeacus prayed to his father, Zeus, for help when there was hardly anyone or anything left alive on the island except the ants. Looking at them, marching along on the ground, he wished that they could become people. Perhaps Zeus was listening, for the next day Aeacus woke to see a great multitude of people, crying allegiance to him, gathered like myriad ants outside the palace gates. Aeacus called his new people Myrmidons, from the Greek word for ants, and they were a hard working and thrifty people, brave in battle.

Ants are well known for their hard work and thrift. They live in a complex and well ordered society.

A RIVER

Selemnus was a shepherd who loved Argyra, an Arcadian nymph of fountains. Argyra returned the boy's love for a while and then grew tired of him. Selemnus grieved so much that

Aphrodite took pity on him and changed him into a river. But that did not help. Selemnus mourned still. So the goddess took away his memory and, ever after that, those who bathed in the river Selemnus were cured of the sorrows of love that was not returned, for they could no longer remember the pain.

A LOTUS TREE

One day, a nymph by the name of Lotis, fleeing from the attentions of an admirer, came to a lake and could go no further. So she turned herself into a lotus tree for protection. It happened that a girl named Driope came down to the lake,

39

Lotus "Coral gem"

with her sister and a baby. Seeing the lovely tree in full blossom, she plucked some of the flowers to make a garland for the baby but, to her horror, she saw blood dripping from each place where she had picked the blossom. She got to her feet to run but found that she could not move. Her sister watched helplessly as her body turned to bark. Poor Driope only had time to tell her sister to let the baby play in her shade but never to pluck a flower from a tree in case it was really a person, before she too became a lotus tree.

The lotus is a plant that loves the sun. Its leaves are silver and its flowers blood red and exotic.

A DIVER BIRD

Aesacus married Astrope, the daughter of a river god. But he really loved her sister, Hesperia. One day, seeing her while out walking, he gave chase. As the girl fled, she stumbled, fell, was bitten by a snake and died. Filled with remorse, Aesacus tried to kill himself by diving into the sea. He was saved by Tithys, a goddess of the Sea, who turned him into a diver bird. The black throated diver bird can be found on the shores of Thessaly, in northern Greece. They are the most primitive birds in Europe. Powerful swimmers. they will rarely be found on land, except for breeding purposes.

The diver bird

Mouflon

A GOLDEN RAM

A certain king, Bisaltes, had a daughter, Theophane, who was so beautiful that the palace was always filled with young men, seeking her hand in marriage. Poseidon, god of the Sea, loved the girl and, to keep her away from the suitors, abducted her to the island of Crumissa. But the young men tracked her down and soon besieged the island.

Poseidon turned Theophane into a ewe, all those on the island into sheep and himself into a ram. Theophane gave birth to a golden ram, whose fleece became the object of Jason's quest with his famous crew, the Argonauts. Wild sheep or mouflon still survive on some Mediterranean islands, including Cyprus.

AN ALMOND TREE

Acamus, son of Theseus, left with Agamemnon's fleet, to fight in the Trojan war, leaving behind his sorrowful wife, Phyllis. The war lasted many years but at last the ships began to put into harbour. Phyllis spent many hours, eagerly scanning the seas, waiting for the return of her husband. Eventually she gave up and died of grief, when Athena turned her into an almond tree.

Wild boar

The very next day Acamus returned home and found nothing but the bare little tree. He embraced it and it burst into flower, although it had not produced leaves.

To this day the lovely tree bears pale pink flowers in early spring, before its dark green leaves

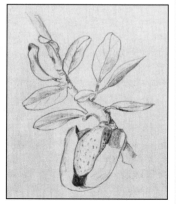

The almond tree

appear. The almond has been cultivated in the Mediterranean area since ancient times. Almond oil is used in medicines and cosmetics.

PIGS

Circe, the enchantress daughter of Helios, god of the Sun, lived on the island of Aeaea. When Odysseus landed there, on his journey home from the Trojan war, he sent his crew ashore to survey the island and look for fresh water. They found Circe's house and she enticed them close before turning them all into pigs. When Odysseus went to search for them he met a young man, the god Hermes in disguise, who gave him a potion of herbs, an anti-dote to Circe's magic. The enchantress fell in love with Odysseus and changed his crew back into men, but all of them more good looking than they had been. Odysseus remained with Circe, on her island, for a year, no doubt under some other of her spells. The wild boar is related to the domestic pig and perhaps this is what Odysseus' crew became. The boar can be found in northern and central Greece still.

DOLPHINS

The god of Wine, Dionysus, walking on the shores of the island of Naxos, was captured by pirates and carried back to their ship. Not knowing who he was and intending to sell him as a slave, they

Dolphins

tied him to the mast. The god took his revenge by turning the sea into wine, dark and sweet. The sails of the ship became vines , thick with fruit and the oars were writhing

serpents. Dionysus himself took on the form of a ferocious lion and the pirates leapt overboard in terror. As they broke the surface of the sea the god changed them into dolphins.

The bottle nosed dolphin is a sociable animal, unafraid of humans, playful and usually occurring in small groups. It feeds mainly on fish and lives for about thirty years.

A SWAN AND AN ISLAND

Zeus fell in love with Leto, a goddess of the night. She spurned his advances but the determined god changed himself into a graceful swan,

43

Mute swan

irresistible to Leto. However, when a few weeks later she discovered that she was pregnant, Zeus abandoned her. But that was not the only trouble Leto had to cope with. Hera was angry. In a jealous rage she hounded poor Leto, the girl running from her but finding that, as no one wanted to incur the wrath of Hera, she could find no shelter. At last she was taken in by her sister, Asteria. Asteria had once angered Zeus by paying no attention to him and he had transformed her into the island of Ortygia. There, Leto gave birth, but only after nine days of agony when Hera prevented the goddess of Childbirth from reaching the island. At last, twins were born. They were Artemis, goddess of Hunting and Apollo, god of Light.

The mute swan winters in Greece and can be found in shallow coastal waters, estuaries and swamps as well as fresh water lakes.

A FIR TREE

Cybele was the goddess of Caverns and she fell in love with Attis, a young shepherd.

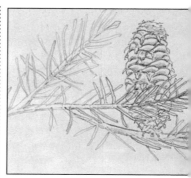

Greek fir

She made him her priest, insisting that he take a vow of chastity. But Attis met the daughter of a river god and broke the vow. Cybele punished him by making him go mad, when he cut off his own genitals. On recovering from the fit, seeing what he had done, he tried to kill himself, but Cybele turned him into a fir tree.

The Greek fir grows in forests on mountains over 800 metres. This tree was used for the wooden columns of the palace of Knossos, on Crete.

ROCKS AND AN IVORY STATUE

Pygmalion was a sculptor, living on the island of Cyprus,

who was happy in his work but avoided his fellow man, hating women in particular. Legend says that he disliked all females because of the behaviour of a certain group of girls who had refused to recognise Aphrodite as divine. They were filled with a shameless desire for the opposite sex, offering themselves to any man who passed by. Aphrodite turned them into rocks.

Now Pygmalion, a fervent worshipper of Aphrodite, was disgusted with the conduct of the girls. He threw himself into his work , chipping away at a piece of ivory. Slowly, under his clever fingers, there grew a statue of an incredibly beautiful woman. He fell in love with it, but it could not respond to his caresses. He dressed his statue in finest linens. He fashioned a necklace from the tear drops of amber which fell from the poplar trees, once the sisters of Phaeton. One day Aphrodite took pity on the sculptor and, when he embraced his statue, it became warm, moved and returned his kisses. Pygmalion called her Galatea, they married and had two sons.

SNAKES, A WINGED HORSE AND WILD BEASTS

Medusa was one of three beautiful sisters, daughters of sea gods, and many men fell in love with her, but it was Poseidon, god of Sea and Horses, who gained her attention and lay with her one day. The great goddess Athena, jealous of Medusa's beauty and of her love for Poseidon, turned the maiden's hair into snakes and made her face so hideous that no man could look at her without being turned to stone.

45

Pegasus

When the hero, Perseus, eventually managed to sever her head, the winged horse, Pegasus, sprang from her neck. Perseus, with winged sandals on his feet, flying back to Sisophon, spilled some drops of blood from Medusa's head, which he carried in a leather purse, onto the Libyan desert. From those drops sprang the wild beasts that inhabit Africa.

The winged horse, Pegasus, is famous in Greek mythology. You will read of how it helped Bellerophon kill the Chimaera, in the section on Monsters.

STARS, DOVES AND CONSTELLATIONS

Orion was a giant from Boetia but, unlike our popular image of giants, he was very good looking. He chased the seven daughters of Atlas and Pleione for five years until they could flee from him no longer. As Orion reached the exhausted girls, Zeus turned them into doves and put their image in the sky as the seven Pleiades.

Orion then fell in love with Merope, but her father, Oenopion, would not allow a marriage, so Orion took the girl by force. Oenopion called to Dionysus for help. You will be reading, later, about how the god made the giant fall into a deep sleep, when Oenopion gouged out his eyes.

With the help of advice from an oracle, Orion's sight was restored and he went to Crete where he hunted with the goddess Artemis, but he boasted that he had killed all the wild aimals on the island and Artemis caused a scorpion to sting him to death. Asclepius tried to restore him to life but was struck by a thunderbolt from Zeus, who considered the power of life over death to be his alone. Orion was changed into the constellation Orion and placed in the sky where he shines brightly until Scorpio appears.

A CUCKOO AND A CHANGE OF SEX

Poseidon loved the nymph, Caeris, and promised her anything she wished for. She was tired of being a woman, she told him, and asked him to make her a bold and invulnerable warrior. So Caeris became the man, Caereus, who was eventually chosen by the Lapith people as their ruler. But he became too proud of his prowess as a warrior and

Cuckoo

prevented the people from worshipping the gods. Instead, he had them worship a spear which he had erected in the market place. An angry Zeus sent the Centaurs to kill him, but Poseidon had made him invulnerable and their weapons were of no avail. In the end, they hammered Caereus into the ground, using tree trunks, which they piled on top of him, once he was well buried. Out of the trunks flew his spirit in the form of a cuckoo and, when the people dug up the body for burial, it was that of a woman. A solitary bird, the cuckoo is well known for its song which heralds the spring, and for its habit of laying its eggs in the nests of other birds. It is a summer visitor to Greece.

THE FIRST HERMAPHRODITE

Hermes and Aphrodite had a son who closely resembled both his father and his mother. His very name belonged to both of them, for he was called Hermaphroditus. When he reached manhood, Hermaphroditus set out to explore the world. One day, when he was in the land of the Carians, he came upon a pool where a beautiful nymph, Salmacis, was gathering flowers. When she caught sight of the boy she fell in love with him at once and, plucking up her courage, she spoke to him, asking if he was free to marry her. Hermaphroditus was embarassed and begged her to leave.

Salmacis pretended to go, but hid herself behind some trees which overhung the pool. The boy, feeling the heat of the summer's day, decided to bathe in the cool water and stripping off his clothes, dived in. At the sight of his lovely

47

young body, the nymph stepped out of her hiding place and, plunging into the water, swam over to Hermaphroditus, twining herself around the reluctant boy and praying to the gods that she might never be separated from him. And so their two bodies became one, neither male nor female. Hermaphroditus, horrified at his weak and effeminate body, asked the gods to grant him one wish; that all who bathed in the pool would be affected in the same way. His wish was granted.

A SNOW WHITE RAVEN

Many years ago, so the story goes, the raven was a snow white bird. One day, as it flew over the plains of Thessaly, it

A white raven

caught sight of the lovely maiden, Coronis, beloved of the god Apollo. She was lying with a young Thessalonian and the raven changed course and set out for Delphi, to carry news of the unfaithful girl to Apollo.

The betrayed god, in a moment of rage, snatched up his bow and let fly an arrow, fatally wounding Coronis. As she lay dying, the heartbroken Apollo cradled her in his arms while she told him that he had killed not one but two, for she was expecting his child.

Unable to save Coronis, Apollo snatched the child from her womb as she lay on the funeral pyre, giving the child to Chiron, the Centaur, to raise.

The raven waited patiently for his reward. But Apollo hated it for bringing the news, blaming it for the death of Coronis. He declared that all ravens should be black from that day on.

The raven is Europe's largest all black bird, as large as a buzzard. It likes open and hilly country, especially sea coasts where it likes to nest on rocky ledges.

48

Pipistrelle bat

BATS

The daughters of Minyas refused to worship Dionysus, god of Wine. On his festival they would not celebrate his rites, choosing, instead, to remain indoors, working at their weaving. But as they worked, the looms turned green, the threads became the tendrils of the vine, leaves grew from the shuttles and bunches of grapes hung heavy from their tapestries.

It was evening, the house shook and the frightened girls hid in the dark corners of the room as their lamps grew smoky. In the thick darkness they crouched as they shrank, their skin stretched and became wings and their voices grew thin until they could only squeak. The angry god had turned them into bats, to fly only at night, crouching in dark corners during the day.

The common pipistrelle bat likes to roost in dark corners of buildings, emerging about half and hour after sunset.

A POISONOUS PLANT

Heracles, that great hero, was sent by the king, Eurystheus,

Worf's bane

to the Underworld. There, he had to find and bring back to the king the terrible three headed dog, Cerberus. As the hero dragged the dog out of the shadowy entrance to those nether regions, the creature struggled to get free and, in its rage, it foamed from its three mouths, sprinkling the fields with flecks of white spittle. Where the froth fell, the white aconite grew.

We know this plant as wolfsbane or monkshood. It bears hooded flowers in the summer and its roots are poisonous.

FROGS

The goddess, Leto, mother of Apollo and Artemis, was fleeing with her children from the wrath of Hera. She came to a lake in a beautiful valley and, being thirsty, bent to take a drink from the cool waters. However, she was prevented by peasants who were working there and who regarded the lake as their own.

Leto explained that water belonged to everyone, provided by Nature, for all to enjoy her refreshing drink. She pleaded for her thirsty children but the peasants still would not let her

Frog

drink.

The angry goddess swore that the people would never escape from the lake. They were filled with a desire to jump into the water and as they swam, they found themselves leaping about, shreiking, their stomachs growing fat and their skin green. They had turned into bickering, croaking frogs.

The edible frog is widespread in Europe and seldom leaves its fresh water home.

A STONE PLANT

The Gorgan, Medusa, was the hideous monster with snakes for hair and any one who looked at her was immediately turned to stone.

You will remember that the hero, Perseus, having killed Medusa, set out for home with her head. On his way he saved the lovely Andromeda, who had been tied to a rock and left to the mercy of a sea monster. Perseus slew the monster and wished to cleanse the blood from his hands by washing in the sea. He set Medusa's head on a pile of leaves on the shore, covering it with a freshly picked weed from the sea.

The weed, still alive, turned to stone on contact with the Gorgon's head, becoming like a brittle tree.

Coral, red, pink and white, is formed by the secretions of marine polyps. Soft and tree-like under water, it hardens when it leaves the sea.

A MOUNTAIN

Perseus continued on his way home, but stopped at the edge of the world for a rest.

Atlas was a huge man who ruled the kingdom at the edge of the world. In his realm was the garden where the trees grew golden apples, cared for by the children of Night, the Hesperides. Atlas had heard it said, one day, that he would lose his golden apples to a son of Zeus, so he guarded them carefully and refused Perseus permission to rest in his kingdom. But Perseus pulled out the head of Medusa and showed it to Atlas who immediately turned to stone. He became a great mountain, on which the whole of the sky rested.

Part 2
MONSTERS

INTRODUCTION

The mythical world of the ancient Greeks was populated not only with powerful gods, goddesses and beautiful nymphs, but also with monsters, most of which, but not all, were terrible to behold. Many of these creatures sprang directly from the seed of Gaia.

Gaia, or Mother Earth, united with her son, Uranus, to produce the Titans, amongst whom were Cronus, the Cyclopes and the Hechatoncheires. These latter offspring were so monstrous that the horrified Gaia, wanting no more, helped her son, Cronus, to overthrow his father by giving him a sharp sickle with which he cut off Uranus' genitals. From the drops of blood which fell to the ground from the dreadful wound, grew a race of giants.

Gaia united with her son Pontus and from the grandchildren of this union came the Gorgons, the Graea and the Harpies. By now seemingly unworried at the creatures she was bearing, or perhaps angry at Zeus' treatment of the Titans and their monster brothers (you will read about this shortly), Gaia united with Tartarus, son of Chaos, to produce Typhoeus, a particularly terrible monster.

We will meet all of these creatures and some of their offspring which were just as dreadful, in the stories which follow.

THE CYCLOPES

The Cyclopes were first heard of in Greek mythology as three sons of Gaia and Uranus. Although sons of gods, they were not immortal. Huge creatures, they were human-like but had only one eye apiece and that in the centre of their foreheads. Their names were Arges, Brontes and Steropes.

You have already read that Cronus, the Titan, overthrew Uranus and became leader of the gods. Worried about the immense strength of his monstrous brothers, the Cyclopes and the Hecatoncheires, Cronus imprisoned them in a place called Tartarus, at the centre of the earth. But later, Cronus' son, Zeus, drove his father out and established

Cyclop

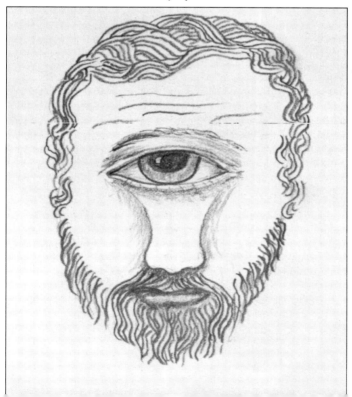

53

himself on Mount Olympus God of the gods. The Titans rebelled and a terrible war followed. Zeus released the Cyclopes and the Hecatoncheires from Tartarus and, with their help, the Titans were defeated, for they not only lent their great strength to the struggle, but the Cyclopes forged the famous thunderbolts of Zeus.

Artemis, the goddess of Hunting, visited the Cyclopes in their workshops where they were working on a trough for Poseidon, god of the Sea. They interrupted their work to make a silver bow and arrow in return for the first beast that the goddess killed with her new weapons.

Legend has it that the Cyclopes built the massive stone walls, called to this day cyclopean walls, of Mycenae and Tiryns. But it was through Apollo, son of Zeus, that the Cyclopes met their death, for he killed them in an act of revenge for forging the thunderbolts with which Zeus slew Asclepius, Apollo's son. We meet the Cyclopes again, however, in later myths from Greece and perhaps they were

distant offspring of the three sons of Gaia and Uranus. These later Cyclopes were also huge one-eyed creatures, who lived wildly in the caves and forests of Sicily. Odysseus, on his long and difficult voyage home from the Trojan war, was taken prisoner, with his crew, by a Cyclop named Polyphemus who lived on human flesh. The men were found by Polyphemus feasting in a cave on food that, unknown to them, belonged to the Cyclop. The giant had driven his flock of sheep into the cave and sealed the entrance with a great stone, before discovering Odysseus and his men. Odysseus tried speaking quietly to his captor but two of his men were eaten at once, in response. His appetite satisfied for a while, the monster slept for the night but ate two more sailors for his breakfast. When yet two more of his crew had been eaten, Odysseus thought to offer the Cyclop some of his wine. Never having tasted anything stronger than sheep's milk, the giant enjoyed his first taste, asked for more and soon fell into a drunken stupor. Odysseus took a brand from the fire and burned out Polyphemus' one eye. As the Cyclop writhed in agony, Odysseus and his remaining   men   escaped, clinging to the bellies of the sheep as they left the cave to graze.

THE HECATONCHEIRES

The Hecatoncheires, brothers of the Cyclopes, were gigantic creatures with fifty heads and one hundred arms each.   Their   names   were Briareus, Gyes and Cottus and you have read how they were imprisoned with the Cyclopes in Tartarus. Zeus released them to help in the war against the Titans, but they were so terrible that, when the epic struggle was over and Zeus had banished the Titans to the centre of the earth, he returned the Hecatoncheires with them, as their guards. Some said   that   their   violent movements, deep inside the earth, were the cause of earthquakes.

Briareus returned to the upper earth once. He was brought up by the goddess Thetis when his hundred hands came in useful to aid Zeus, who had been bound tightly by his jealous wife,

Hera, as a punishment for his many infidelities.

THE GIANTS

The Giants, who grew up from the blood which fell from the terrible wound of the castrated Uranus, had legs of serpents with the reptiles' heads for their feet. After Zeus had won the struggle for power against the Titans, the Giants rose up against him. They advanced on Mount Olympus and a fearful battle commenced, but an oracle had predicted that only a mortal would defeat the monsters.

The goddess Athena, therefore, asked that great hero, Heracles, for help. One of the giants, Alcyoneus, was immortal, but only when in his own land of Pallene. Heracles dragged him from there and killed him before turning   his   attention   to Porphyrion, who was wounded by a thunderbolt from Zeus. Heracles finished him off with an arrow. Ephialtes was shot in one eye by Apollo and in the other by Heracles. In this way, one by one the giants were defeated and Zeus reigned supreme once more.

PYTHON

Python was a huge, female dragon-like serpent which guarded the Oracle of Gaia, at the foot of Mount Parnassus. Apollo, armed with arrows made for him by the smith god, Hephaestus, killed it in revenge for its treatment of his mother. He purified himself in the Vale of Tempe before returning to take charge of the Oracle, which, as you will read in Part Three, became the Delphic Oracle.

Every nine years, in a festival which took place at Delphi, the scene was re-enacted and a young man would deem it a great honour to be chosen to play the part of Apollo.

Python

TYPHOEUS

Typhoeus was one of the most frightening of monsters. The offspring, as we have said, of Gaia and Tartarus, it was a creature with a hundred dragons' heads which breathed fire. Myriad snakes sprouted from its thighs and its body was feathered.

All the gods ran from this monster in terror. All, that is, except for Athena. She persuaded Zeus to return and fight Typhoeus, but the god became entwined in the coils of the snakes and lay helpless as the creature cut the sinews to his hands and feet. The god Hermes came to the rescue and Zeus was at last able to hurl his thunderbolts at the monster until he had driven it to Sicily,

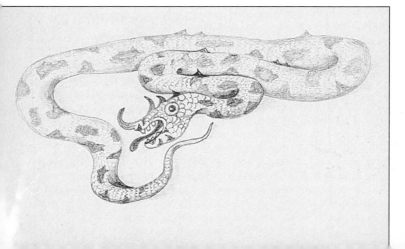

where he crushed it under Mount Etna. The dragons' heads still breathe fire from under the mountain.

SCYLLA

Scylla was a beautiful young nymph and a sea god, Glaucus, fell in love with her. But Circe, a sorceress, was very jealous, turning Scylla into a hideous beast with six long necks growing out of her shoulders, each topped with six dog-like heads which had great rows of terrible teeth.

This monster, Scylla, took up residence in a cave in a place still known as Scilla, in Italy, today. This place juts out into the narrow straits between Sicily and the mainland, known now as the Straits of Messina. There she waited, ready to devour any passing sailor, snatching the unfortunate man from the deck of his ship as the vessel passed through the channel. She made a meal of six of Odysseus' crew in this way, before being turned into a rock.

TITYUS

Some say that Tityus was a son of Gaia and others say that he was born from a union between Zeus and the mortal, Elare. One way or another, Tityus grew to be a giant of enormous proportions. Leto was the mother of the twins, Apollo and Artemis. Hated by Hera, legend has it that Tityus was sent by that jealous goddess to rape her. Apollo and Artemis shot him and condemned him to be punished in Hades for eternity. He was laid out on the ground, where it is said that his body covered nine acres, and vultures pecked for ever at his liver which grew back each month.

ECHIDNE AND ARGUS PANOPTES

Echidne was a monster, half snake and half nymph, who lived in a cave from which she would pounce on passers by and eat them. Born out of the seed of Gaia, she herself bore a terrible brood when she mated with Typhoeus. She never grew old but was not immortal, eventually being killed by Argus Panoptes. Argus Panoptes was a giant with one hundred eyes, of which fifty remained on watch while the other fifty slept. He served Hera faithfully as her watchman and when he was killed by Hermes,

Echidne

the goddess took his eyes and set them in the tail of her favourite bird, the peacock, where you will see them to this day.

THE SPHINX

The Sphinx was a female monster which had a woman's head, the body of a lion and the wings of a bird. A daughter of Echidne and Typhoeus, she plagued the city of Thebes by eating all those who could not answer a riddle. What was it, she asked, that walked at dawn on four legs, at midday on two and on three at twilight? The young prince, Oedipus, arriving in Thebes and finding the people near to despair, faced the Sphinx and answered the riddle. Man, he said, crawled on all fours as a baby, then walked on two legs before using a stick in his old age. The Sphinx, furious that the puzzle had been solved, threw herself from the walls of the city, to be dashed to death on the rocks below.

THE CHIMAERA

Another offspring of Typhoeus and Echidne was the Chimaera. It had the head of a lion, the body of a goat and the tail of a serpent. It breathed fire and terrorized the people of Lycia, until the gods helped a young man, Bellerophon, to kill it. The goddess Athena gave Bellerophon a golden, magic bridle which enabled him to catch the winged horse, Pegasus, that, as you will have read in part one, sprang from the head of Medusa.

The Sphinx

Mounted on the famous steed, Bellerophon flew over the awesome, fire breathing monster, dropping lead into its mouth. The lead melted in the heat of the flames and choked the monster to death.

Unfortunately, Bellerophon"s life ended tragically. He grew too proud of his feats and thought to place himself with the gods, on Olympus. He flew there on Pegasus, but Zeus flung him back to earth. Injured by the fall, Bellerophon limped about the earth, friendless, ignored by all until he died, for who would dare speak to one who had offended

The Chimaera

the god of gods?

THE GORGONS

Phorcys, a sea god, and Ceto, the pretty-cheeked, were two children of Gaia and Pontus. The brother and sister united to produce the Gorgons and, as can be expected of an incestuous relationship, one legend has it that three monsters were born as a result, the Gorgons, although according to some tales, these three began life as lovely maidens until they each offended the gods in some way. The three were named Stethno, Euryale and Medusa. Winged females, some said that they had bronze claw-like hands, great tusks for teeth, lolling tongues and snakes for hair. Only Medusa was mortal and she was put to death, with the help of the gods, by Perseus and you will read the full story of this exploit in part three.

THE GRAEAE

These were the other children of Phorcys and Ceto. Not as terrible as the Gorgons, they were three swan-like, grey-haired creatures who had only one eye and one tooth between them. When Perseus was hunting for Medusa, he had to snatch the eye from them before

A Centaur

they would tell him where their monstrous sister could be found.

CENTAURS

Centaurs were half horse, half man and were descendants of the god Ares. they had a reputation for wild drunkenness, but nevertheless they were invited, by the Lapith king, Pierithous, to his wedding feast. Unfortunately, the wine went to their heads and they tried to carry off the women. The result was war and the Centaurs were driven from the Lapith country, to take refuge in the Peloponnese.

Not all the Centaurs were so ill mannered, however. One day, one of their number, a certain Pholus, was entertaining Heracles in Arcadia. His fellow Centaurs though, smelled the wine as it was being poured and went on the rampage. The great Heracles chased them away and they hid on Mount Malea.

Another gentle Centaur was

Cheiron. Learned and a lover of music and medicine, he was immortal. He lived on Mount Pelion and many of the great Greek heroes were sent there, to learn from him. Legend had it that he was shot, by mistake, by Heracles. The arrow pierced his foot and the wound gave him so much pain that he wished for death. His immortality should have made it impossible but perhaps Zeus took pity on him, allowing him to die before placing him in the heavens as the constellation Centaurus.

The Minotaur

THE MINOTAUR

King Minos of Crete sorely offended the god, Poseidon, by refusing to sacrifice a fine bull to the deity. The angry Poseidon caused Minos' wife, Pasiphae, to fall in love with the bull. The result of the love affair, carried out with the aid of a hollow wooden cow in which Pasiphae lay, was the birth of the Minotaur, a monster with the head of a bull and the body of a man. The creature was so fearsome that King Minos had a complicated labyrinth built, in the middle of which he imprisoned the Minotaur. The monster was fed with young boys, brought over every nine years from Athens, until it was killed by Theseus. You will read how Theseus managed this with the help of Minos' daughter, Ariadne, in part three.

LADON

At the very western edge of the world, so the legend says, was a fabulous garden where golden apples grew. It was guarded by the Hesperides, lovely daughters of Atlas. When the goddess, Hera, discovered that the girls were helping themselves to the fruit, she sent Ladon, a dragon with one hundred heads, to sit beneath the trees so that no-one could go near. Ladon was yet another offspring of that terrible pair, Echidne and Typhoeus. Heracles killed Ladon with one of his famous arrows when, as one of his twelve labours, he had to collect the golden apples from the garden and take them back to Tiryns and King Eurystheus.

Ladon

GERYON AND ORTHRUS

Geryon was a huge man with three bodies, three heads and six hands. He lived at the far west of the world and guarded a wonderful herd of cattle. Orthrus was a two headed dog which helped Geryon to guard the cattle. Some say he was the father of the Sphinx. Heracles was sent to steal the cattle as one of his labours. He ws successful but we are told little of the fierce battle that must have taken place between two of the strongest men alive. Heracles slew Orthrus and eventually Geryon was fatally wounded by one of the hero's arrows. From the blood that fell from the wound, some say, grew a tree which fruited when the Pleiades rose in the sky. The link is that these stars depict the seven granddaughters of the god Oceanus, born from his daughter Pleione. Geryon was the son of Oceanus' daugher, Callirhoe.

63

Talus

hurling rocks at anyone who approached. Whatever his shape, ichor, instead of blood, flowed in his only vein which ended in one ankle, where it was closed by a bronze nail.

When Jason and his Argonaut crew were sailing home from their quest for the golden fleece, they met Talus, who threw his customary rocks at them. But Jason was accompanied by the sorceress, Medea, who used her magical powers to cause the great bronze giant to graze his ankle. The nail fell out, the ichor pouring from the hole until Talus sunk to the ground and died.

TALUS

The god Cronus ruled the Golden age of man. A silver age followed and, afterwards, there arose a brazen race, warlike men of bronze, giants in fact, and Talus was reputed to be the last of them. Some say that he had the head of a bull and he guarded the island of Crete,

DELPHYNE

This was a she-dragon, friend of Python who guarded the Oracle of Gaia. When Typhoeus coiled his serpents around Zeus and severed the sinews to the god's hands and feet, the monster dragged his victim to a cave and hid the sinews in a bear skin. He put Delphyne to guard them. But Hermes took the god Pan along to the cave. Pan gave a great shout, filling the

Delphyne

monster with panic and Hermes was able to slip past it unnoticed, take the sinews and put them back into the limbs of Zeus.

It is said that Delphyne was killed by Apollo when he slew the Python before taking over the Oracle from Gaia.

CERBERUS

Cerberus was another dreadful child of Typhoeus and Echidne. He was a huge, savage dog with three heads and he guarded the entrance to Hades. He had a serpent's tail and snake heads growing from his back. He allowed spirits to enter Hades but ate anyone who tried to leave.

Heracles was sent, on one of his labours, to bring the monstrous hound to King Eurystheus. The hero succeeded but, on seeing it, the king ordered Heracles to return it to the Underworld.

Cerberus could be pacified with cakes, honey and even music. Orpheus, son of Apollo, was a wonderful musician who, when his wife died, resolved to go down to the Underworld and bring her back. It was a terrifying journey but, when he reached those nether regions, the beauty of his music calmed Hades, the Furies and even the monster, Cerberus. Orpheus took his wife but was told that, as he left with her, he must not look back. Orpheus had almost reached the upper world when, without thinking, he glanced behind to make sure that his wife was following. At once she disappeared and even the sweet lyre of Orpheus could not get her past Cerberus a second time.

THE HARPIES

Harpies were female monsters with the heads of women and the wings of birds. Swift, equipped with long talons, they snatched food, infecting what they did not take, causing it to rot so fast that it was inedible within seconds. They were sometimes called "the hounds of Zeus".

Phineus was a soothsayer who upset Zeus. He was punished by the god and condemned to

A Harpy

starve. Whenever he sat down to eat, the Harpies arrived, snatched at his food and ruined it.

Jason and his Argonaut crew came across Phineus when they were searching for the golden fleece. To help the starving soothsayer, they enlisted the help of the sons of the North Wind, who chased the Harpies and would have killed them had not the rainbow goddess, Iris, intervened, promising that the harpies would not bother Phineus again. So Jason and his men sat down to a great feast with the seer before continuing on their way.

THE ERINNYES

These were hideous creatures with serpents for hair and they were born, with the Giants, from the blood of the castrated Uranus. They took revenge on those who killed their parents and were famous for hounding Orestes, son of Agamemnon, who killed his mother, Clytaemnestra, after she and her lover had slain his father. In spite of the fact that he was avenging his father's death, the Erinnyes drove Orestes mad.

66

The Nemean Lion

THE NEMEAN LION

This great lion was another of the children of Typhoeus and Echidne, although some legends say that it was the result of a relationship between Zeus and the lovely Moon goddess, Silene who, horrified at what she bore, dropped it to earth from the moon. It fell near Nemea and ravaged the surrounding countryside. No-one dared attempt to kill it, for its skin repelled all weapons.

Heracles was sent to rid the land of the Nemean lion, as one of his labours. When he found that his arrows failed to pierce its hide, he had to resort to fighting the monster with his bare hands. Heracles succeeded in killing the lion but lost a finger in the fray.

He skinned the beast and wore the pelt ever after, as armour.

THE TELCHINES

These were nine children of the sea, who had dogs' heads and flippers for hands. They were said to have forged the sickle with which Cronus castrated Uranus. They cared for the infant Poseidon and made his trident. But the Telchines had the audacity to interfere with the weather, conjuring mists and making rain, hail and thunderstorms. They caused such havoc that Zeus decided to send a flood to destroy them. The goddess Artemis warned the nine Telchines and they fled the land, but Zeus caught some of them in a deluge and Apollo, disguised as a wolf, destroyed the rest.

Cetus

THE CALEDONIAN BOAR

A certain kin, Oenus, forgot to sacrifice to Artemis one year, at harvest time. As a punishment, the angry goddess sent a terrible, monstrous boar to destroy the crops, kill cattle and devour men. Eventually the desperate king organised a great hunt, inviting the bravest men in the land to take part. Meleager, son of Oenus, killed the boar but Atlanta, a beautiful huntress from Arcadia, drew first blood. You will have read what happened to Meleager as a result, in Part One.

CETUS

The king of Ethiopia had a lovely daughter, Andromeda. Unfortunately, Andromeda's mother, Cassiopeia, boasted that she was more beautiful than the daughter of Nereus, as sea god. As a punishment for being so rash, the great god of the Sea, Poseidon, sent a monster, Cetus, to devour the Ethiopians. When the gods were asked to be merciful, they demanded that Andromeda be chained to a rock in the sea, as food for the monster.

Perseus, on his way home from killing the Gorgon, Medusa, saw the lovely maiden tied to the rock and fell in love with her. As the monster approached for its meal, Perseus took up his sword and slew it, winning Andromeda for his wife.

THE STYMPHALIAN BIRDS

These birds lived in a marshy lake in Arcadia. They were huge, with bronze beaks and claws and they lived on human flesh. If they all flew into the air together, they blotted out the sun. The local people were terrified of them and it took Heracles, on one of his labours, to get rid of them.

THE EMPUSAE

Empusa

These were children of Hecate, a goddess of Darkness. They were half ass with, so it was said, one bronze leg and one ass's leg. They were seductive females who could take on any form and, thus disguised, would approach men while they slept, sucking life out of them, vampire-like.

TRITONS

Triton, so one legend goes, was a gentle sea god, son of Poseidon. He had the tail of a fish and calmed the seas by blowing on a conch shell. But another tale, from Boeotia, tells of Tritons who were monstrous beasts with human heads bearing gills and mouths containing the teeth of animals. Their scaly bodies had the tails of dolphins. They enjoyed a drink and they would attack boats unless wine was put out for them.

69

Triton

Part 3
ORACLES

INTRODUCTION

An oracle, according to the Concise Oxford Dictionary, is a "place at which ancient Greeks etc. were accustomed to consult their deities for advice and prophecy" or "the response, often ambiguous or obscure, given at such a place".
Many variations exist of these stories of the Oracle at Delphi and of nearly all the tales involving myth and legend. Some contradict each other, so I have wended my way through the labyrinth of accounts, choosing those which seem to tie together or simply were, to me, the most appealing or interesting. Where some stories link, the connection has, in some cases, been made by myself, but only in the mythological tales. I have not tampered with history. Some attempt has been made to give an idea of the passage of time, but the gods of ancient Greece were timeless and immortal. If we want to put Delphi and its Oracle into the context of time, we must go back 3,500 years, to a Mycenaean settlement which existed there around 1600 BC. Its people were known to be devoted to Gaia, Mother Earth, but perhaps her cult was older than that, as traces of Stone Age man have been found at the site.

We must wonder at the story of Deucalion and the flood. The Mediterranean basin, which had been dry for a million years, flooded for the last time just over 5,000,000 years ago. Man as we know him did not appear until long after that, yet the story of the flood belongs to many cultures. Deucalion and his wife re-populated the earth with stones and, according to one Greek legend, those pebbles became Stone Age man. Was the story of the flood an ancient memory, buried deep in the genes of those ape-like ancestors of Homo Sapiens and passed down over millions of years? Was the story contained in what Jung calls the "collective unconscious of

Magic, Monsters and Oracles from the Greek Myths

man"? Most probably the flood had been a local one and the story passed orally down through generations. Who or what were those people who worshipped Gaia before the flood? Perhaps the Mycenaeans found traces of the sea on their mountains and invented the stories as an explanation.

We will never know the answer but the questions make these tales all the more fascinating. Many of them belong to myth and legend, others to history and fact, the rest lying somewhere in-between.

If you visit the sanctuary at Delphi today, you cannot fail to be overawed by the majesty of the setting for Apollo's temple, which is set on the slopes of Mount Parnassus, overlooking the Pleistos valley, grey green with olives. You can walk the Sacred Way which winds its way up to the temple among the ruins of treasuries and monuments, still feeling that you are in a hallowed place.

The spread of Christianity saw the slow decline in the worship of Apollo at Delphi as the pagan deities were frowned upon. The last prophecy, as you will read, was given to the Emperor Julian, when he tried, without success, to bring back the old gods.

THE ORIGIN
OF THE ORACLE

Before time as we know it began, so said the ancient Greeks, Chaos existed, dark and formless. Out of Chaos came Gaia, Mother Earth, who began the creation of the universe with the forming of Uranus, the all embracing sky. Together with Uranus, Gaia produced the first of a race of gods and goddesses, one of whom was a Titan named Cronus, who became ruler of the gods.

Gaia, who possessed the gift of prophecy, forecast that Cronus would be dethroned by one of his sons. The god thought that he could overcome the power of Gaia's words and swallowed each of his children as it was born. But when his wife bore her sixth child, she gave it into the care of Gaia and offered Cronus, ins-tead, a great stone wrapped in a shawl, which the god duly swallowed.

In the care of Mother Earth, the child, named Zeus and destined to become the god of gods, quickly grew to manhood, when he took his revenge on his father. He gave Cronus a draught which caused him to vomit up the stone and the five children. Zeus then overthrew Cronus, banishing him deep into the centre of the earth before releasing two eagles, one from either end of the world and, at the place where they met, at the foot of Mount Parnassus, he placed the stone. It was called the omphalos, meaning the mid point of the earth or, perhaps, the navel of Gaia, the Earth Mother.

Gaia, said the ancient Greeks, not only created the first gods but also gave birth to the human race who worshipped her as Mother Earth. Now Mother Earth breathed, her breath rising from a fissure in the ground where Zeus had placed the stone. Here, a goatherd, guarding his flock on the slopes of Parnassus, was puzzled over the behaviour of his goats which leapt over the break in the earth in a frenzy. Going close to investigate, he was affected in the same way and began to prophecy.

The story of this strange happening spread and all those who approached the place became intoxicated and told the future. The area became renowned locally for miracles and prophecies attributed to Gaia and there she was worshipped. The Oracle was born. A temple was built to Gaia and later to Themis, her daughter, who became the second custodian of the Oracle.

Now Zeus ruled gods and men from his home on Mount Olympus and both races lived in harmony, eating and drinking together until one day a meeting was arranged between the two races, to decide which part of a sacrificial animal should be given to the gods, and which to man. To the immortal Prometheus was given the task of dividing an ox. Prometheus, very much on the side of man, put the best pieces of meat to one side and on the other he laid out the bones, carefully covered with succulent portions of fat. Zeus was invited to take first pick and he flew into a rage when he chose the glossy fat, only to discover bare bones underneath. The god took his revenge by taking fire away from mankind but Prometheus stole it back. The angry Zeus decided to be rid of man once and for all.

He caused the skies to darken and rain began to fall. great drops fell heavily on the earth, saturating the soil. Rivers overflowed, the sea rose and flooded the land, covering the hills and finally the mountains. But Prometheus, whose name meant forethought, had warned his human son, Deucalion. He had told him to build and provision a boat and to take his wife aboard. When the waters began to recede, Deucalion and his wife, Pyrrha, found themselves grounded on the slopes of Mount Parnassus, alone in the world.

As the water level dropped, the pair discovered a temple,

overgrown with weed and almost in ruins. There they offered sacrifice, first to Zeus and then to Themis, giving thanks for their deliverance and praying for help. In answer they heard a voice saying,

"Ungirdle yourselves, cover your heads and throw over your shoulders the bones of your ancestors."

Deucalion had found the ancient temple built to Themis, in the place that would one day be called Delphi. He pondered the words of the Oracle and then he and Pyrrha loosened their robes, covered their heads and began to walk, throwing stones from the ground over their shoulders. Deucalion had rightly interpreted that Gaia, the earth, was their ancestor and that the stones were her bones. As Pyrrha threw the stones they became women and those that Deucalion threw became men and so the world was re-populated.

Gaia and her daughter, Themis, continued to be worshipped on the slopes of Parnassus and a great serpent, Python, guarded the Oracle from his cave nearby. The place was known as Pytho. At first, it is said, the local people visited the strange fissure and prophesied to each other, but after a while a woman was appointed to give voice to the Oracle. A virgin, then later it was always an older woman, called the Pythia, was seated on a tripod over the sacred chasm, to pronounce the words of the goddess.

APOLLO AND THE ORACLE

Zeus fell in love with Leto, as you will have read earlier, seducing her in the form of a swan but abandoning her when he found that she was pregnant. Hera, the wife of Zeus, in a jealous rage, hounded Leto, sending the Python, guardian of the Oracle, in pursuit of her. Letos's problems were not over when at last she was given shelter by her sister, Asteria, who had been turned by Zeus into the floating island of Ortygia, for refusing his attentions. Hera proclaimed that the birth could only occur in a place where the rays of the sun could not penetrate.

ORACLES   *Magic, Monsters and Oracles from the Greek Myths*

The god Poseidon, Lord of the Sea, came to the rescue by covering Ortygia with a dome of waves, anchoring the island to the sea bed with four pillars. The birth imminent, the furious Hera withheld Ilythia, the goddess of childbirth, thus making Leto suffer nine days and nights of agony before Zeus sent the goddess Iris to take Ilythia to the desperate woman. The birth took place at last. Twins were born, Artemis first, followed by Apollo, the Sun god, Delighter in High Places, the Brilliant, god of Light, son of a divinity of the night.

The island of Ortygia was renamed Delos, meaning brilliant and the baby Apollo was taken by Themis, the keeper of the Delphic Oracle, who fed him, not on his mother's milk, but on the food of the gods. So, on a diet of nectar and sweet ambrosia, Apollo reached adulthood in four days. He was ready to avenge the pain of his mother and he set out to kill the Python which had hounded her.

Using arrows forged for him by the Smith god, Hephaestus, Apollo killed the Python in the Parnassus gorge. To purify himself of the blood stains, he

Entrance to Apollo's temple at Delphi

went to wash himself in the Vale of Tempe before returning to Pytho. There, in the sacred grove, he built an altar. Looking for priests to help start his cult of worship, he found the place deserted, but saw, in the distance, a Cretan ship heading out to sea.

Changing himself into a dolphin, he gave chase, turned the ship around and grounded it in the Gulf of Corinth. Returning to human shape, he told the terrified sailors that they were to guard his temple and that, as they had first seen him as a dolphin, they were to call him the Delphinian, from the Greek word for dolphin, "delphini". And so the place Pytho came to be known as Delphi and Themis handed over the custodianship of the Oracle to Apollo.

News of the miraculous prophecies at Delphi spread and people began to come from far and wide to consult the wise and benevolent god who acted as interpreter between his father, Zeus, and the human race. Heroes, that race of people between gods and men, came to seek the Oracle's advice.

Kings, politicians and ordinary people were to approach the sacred place.

Those seeking the Oracle had first to pay a sum of money and then to sacrifice an animal, usually a goat, free from blemish. If the gods found the sacrifice favourable, the seeker was allowed into the temple of Apollo. The priestess or Pythia, was seated in the 'adyton', an underground chamber. The word in modern Greek still means 'inaccessible' and no-one but the priestess was allowed in to this room.

The Pythia had prepared herself for the moment by purifying herself in the Kastalian spring before entering the temple. There, she chewed on a laurel leaf. The laurel was a plant of particular importance to Apollo, and perhaps this induced a state of trance. Certainly it is known that the priestess, when she finally seated herself on the tripod, was in a state of intoxication which some say was a result of breathing in the vapours from the fissure in the earth. From her underground room the Pythia uttered unintelligible mutterings in answer to the questions put to her. These mumblings were interpreted above by a priest who translated them, giving out the Oracle in verse.

CREUSA AND XUTHUS

By this time, through Deucalion and Pyrrha, the earth had been re-populated and one of their descendants, Xuthus by name, fled to Athens after being accused of theft by his brothers. There he met and married Creusa, daughter of a king.

As a young girl, so the old story goes, Creusa had been abducted by Apollo and seduced by him in a dark cave. When she found that she was with child she was terrified, the punishment being death even if her story was believed. It seems that no-one noticed her condition and when the time came, she went back to the cave to have the baby, leaving it there to die. Filled with remorse however, she returned, only to find the cave empty and even her cloak, which she had used to wrap around the baby, was gone. She thought that wolves or other wild animals

must have eaten the child and so her secret was safe.

After some years of marriage, Xuthus, distressed when no children came of the union, decided to go with Creusa to consult the Delphic Oracle and to ask Apollo for a child. When they reached the holy place, Creusa went towards the sanctuary first and on the way, in a courtyard, she met a beautiful boy, dressed as a priest. He told her that his name was Ion and that Apollo's priests had found him and brought him up. When Creusa told him that she was approaching the temple to accuse the god of wronging a woman and to ask how the resulting child had died, the boy was horrified and told Creusa not to go to Apollo's altar in such an angry state of mind.

Xuthus, in the meantime, consulted the Oracle and was told that the first person that he met after leaving the sanctuary, would be his son. Approaching the courtyard, he saw Ion standing with Creusa and with great joy he held his arms out to the boy, saying that Apollo had declared him to be his child. Creusa listened to this exchange with growing bitterness. Not only had she been mis-treated by Apollo, but also her husband had betrayed her and had a child by some other woman. She demanded to know who the mother of Ion was and Xuthus confessed that he did not know, only that the god had gifted him with a son at last.

Leaving the two together, Creusa left the courtyard in disgust. She saw an old priestess approaching and was about to brush her aside when the woman caught at her arm, holding out a cloak, saying that it was to be given to Ion. She said that he had been wrapped in it when he was found. Creusa recognised it as hers and, with joy, realised that Ion was her son.

We are told that Ion returned to Athens with Creusa and Xuthus, on advice from the goddess Athena, who appeared to them at Delphi, saying that she was sent by Apollo to tell them that one day Ion would rule over her city.

Ion married Selina, daughter of the king of Aegialus and some years later he was chosen to be king of Athens. So the Oracle was fulfilled.

The priestess offers the robe

PERSEUS, MEDUSA AND THE ORACLE

Acrisius, king of Argos, had a daughter, Danae, but badly wanted a son. He approached the Oracle, but instead of receiving the advice he expected, he was warned that one day a son of Danae would kill him. To thwart destiny, Acrisius had his daughter locked into a bronze tower and guarded by savage dogs, but Zeus entered her prison through the bars in her window, disguised as a shower of gold, and seduced her. When Danae produced a son whom she named Perseus, her father locked them both into a chest which he threw into the sea.

Zeus guided the chest safely to the shores of the island of Seriphus, where it was found by a fisherman, Dictys. The fisherman escorted Danae and her son to the court of his brother, King Polydectes, who took them both into his home. When Perseus reached manhood, he defended his mother against the lustful Polydectes. The latter, desirous of the beautiful Danae, lied to Perseus, saying that he was really in love with another woman and required a wedding present in the form of horses from all his subjects. He knew that the boy had nothing of his own but Perseus, with the impetuosity of youth, promised to give the king anything he wanted, even the head of the Gorgon, Medusa.

Now the Gorgons were those fearful creatures with hair of snakes and anyone looking at them was turned to stone. So Polydectes accepted the boy's offer happily, certain that he would not survive the quest for Medusa's head and then he himself would be free to turn his amorous attentions to Danae.

Perseus left Seriphus and sailed to Greece. He went to Delphi to ask the Oracle where he could find the Gorgons. The priestess was not much help. She told him to go to the place where acorns were eaten instead of grain. Perseus knew that Zeus spoke an Oracle at Dodona, a place where oak trees grew in abundance and people ate bread made from ground acorns. There he was told simply that the gods would protect him.

And so the gods did. Hermes appeared to him and told him to go to the Graeae, three old women who had only one eye and one tooth between them and who would tell him where to find the Gorgons. Pallas Athena appeared to him and gave him a highly polished bronze shield.

She told him not to look at Medusa when he attacked her, but to watch her mirrored in the shield.

When Perseus found the Graeae, they were reluctant to help him, so he snatched their one eye from them and to get it back they directed him to the land of the Hyperboreans, where the Gorgons lived. The people of that land welcomed Perseus, giving him a cap which, when he wore it, made him invisible and presenting him with a magic purse which adapted its size to whatever was put into it.

Perseus approached the Gorgons and was lucky to find them asleep. Looking into the shield, he cut off the head of Medusa and put it into the purse. Using the magic cap he was able to make good his escape from her angry sisters and make his way back to Seriphus with his trophy.

Back home, he found that his mother had been forced to take refuge in the temple, to escape the attentions of the king. Polydectes himself was feasting with his friends in his palace.

The head of Medusa

Perseus went there and stood before them all, with Athena's bright shield and the magic purse. All eyes were upon him as he showed them Medusa's head. They were immediately turned to stone.

Perseus made Dictys king before setting sail for Argos with his mother Danae, desiring to be reconciled with his father. Acrisius, however, when he heard that they were on their way, thought that Perseus wanted revenge and fled to Larissa. When Perseus arrived in Argos, he was invited to funeral games held in Larissa, in honour of King Teutomides' father. Perseus took part in the throwing of the discus but when he threw, a strong wind caught the discus, which struck a spectator, killing him. It was Acrisius. The Oracle of Delphi had been fulfilled.

Perseus became king of Tiryns and legend has it that one day, while travelling around his realm, he was thirsty. A mushroom or toadstool appeared out of the ground by his feet, together with a stream of water. He quenched his thirst and decided to build a city in that place. He called it after the fungus or myces, naming it Mycenae.

HERACLES AND THE ORACLE

Zeus fell in love with Alcmene, the wife of a general who was away at war. One night the great god disguised himself as Amphitryon, the woman's husband, and spent some hours with her. As soon as he left, Amphitryon himself returned, much to the astonishment of Alcmene, who slept the rest of the night with her own husband. Twins were the result of the night's passion. Iphicles came from the seed of Amphitryon and Heracles was born from the seed of Zeus but hated by Hera, the jealous wife of the god.

One legend says that Zeus put the baby Heracles to suckle at Hera's breast while the goddess slept. When she woke with a start the spilt milk formed the Milky Way. Thus nourished, Heracles grew strong and survived several attempts by Hera to kill him.

Heracles married Megara, the

Heracles and the Nemean Lion

82

daughter of Creon, king of Thebes and they had several children. Unfortunately, the vindictive Hera afflicted Heracles with a fit of madness, making him see his wife and children as enemies and he killed them all. When he recovered himself and saw what he had done, he was horrified and banished himself from Thebes. He went to Delphi to ask the advice of the Oracle. There he was told that to purge himself of the crime, he was to go to Tiryns and perform ten labours for the king, Eurystheus. The Oracle told him that if he succeeded in completing his tasks, he would become immortal, although some say that the breast milk of Hera had already given him immortality.

Eurystheus of Tiryns saw the imposition of the tasks as a good way to be rid of Heracles who, with his great strength, might one day become a threat to him. So the labours he set were formidable. It is said that many of them were suggested by Hera, but certainly the punishment had to fit the crime.

The first task for Heracles was the killing of the Nemean Lion. This was a great beast whose hide repelled all weapons. Heracles sealed off the exit to the animal's cave and, going in through the entrance. strangled the lion with his bare hands. He returned to Tiryns with the beast slung over his shoulder and Eurystheus, who had not really expected to see Heracles again, was so terrified by the sight that he hid in a bronze jar and issued his next orders through his herald.

The king thought of a more difficult task. Heracles had to kill the many headed Hydra, which lived at Lerna. This was a huge serpent-like creature which breathed fire. Where Heracles cut off one head, two others grew in its place and one great head was immortal. The Hydra wound itself around Heracles' feet and when a giant crab came to the creature's aid, Heracles called for his charioteer and nephew, Iolaus, to help. Between them they overcame the beast with fire and Heracles dipped his arrows into its poisonous blood before returning to Tiryns. There, the king refused to recognise the killing of the Hydra as one of the tasks, as Heracles had been helped by Iolaus.

Eurystheus sent Heracles to capture, alive, a hind with a golden horn, knowing full well that it was sacred to the goddess Artemis. The hind was capable of great speed and Heracles hunted it for a year before he was able to capture the exhausted creature near the river Ladon. Carrying it back to Tiryns, he met an angry Artemis who demanded the return of her deer. Heracles must had had charm as well as strength because he persuaded the goddess to let him keep the beautiful creature and he returned with it to Tiryns. A great boar ravaged the area around Mount Erymanthus. Heracles was sent to capture it alive. He hunted it until he was able to drive it into deep snow, when he caught it in a net. Its appearance was so dreadful that when he reached Tiryns with it, Eurystheus again took refuge in his bronze jar. The city was buzzing with the news of the quest for the Golden Fleece and Heracles left for Iolcus to serve on the Argo with Jason, but he eventually had to return to his labours.
Eurystheus, angry at Heracle's temporary departure from the

Heracles and the Golden Hind

city, gave him a degrading task. He was sent to clean out the stables of King Augeias of Elis, which were thick with dung accumulated over the years from a vast herd of cattle. On arriving at Elis, Heracles told Augeias that he would clean out his stables but did not mention to the king that he was under orders and asked for payment for the work. The king agreed and the great Heracles broke the banks of a nearby river and the flood waters swept the stables clear of the dung. Augeias refused to honour his side of the bargain and when Heracles returned to Tiryns, Eurystheus would not recognise the task as valid because Heracles, albeit unsuccessfully, had demanded payment.

On Lake Stymphalia lived a flock

of terrifying birds. Some say that they were man-eating, others that they had bronze beaks and claws and used their feathers as arrows. Heracles was sent to rid the area of the birds. Athena gave him a pair of huge cymbals which the hero clashed together. At the noise, the flocks rose into the air, whereupon Heracles let fly his arrows, tipped with poison from the Hydra, killing them all.

Eurystheus decided to send Heracles further afield. Perhaps he thought that a dangerous journey, coupled with an even more formidable task, would be too much for the hero, whom he sent to Crete to capture alive a great white bull which was terrifying the people of the island. Heracles performed the task and it is said that he made the bull swim from Crete to the mainland while he rode on its back. On reaching Tiryns he freed the bull which eventually reached Marathon where it caused much concern among the local population.

Heracles was ordered to Thrace to bring back the Mares of Diomedes, wild man-eating horses belonging to a savage king. During the battle to win them from Diomedes, a young boy, much loved by Heracles, was eaten by the animals. Heracles killed Diomedes and fed him to the Mares. They became tame as a result and the hero drove them back to Eurystheus.

The queen of the Amazons, Hippolyte, had a magic belt, desired by Eurystheus for his daughter. Heracles was sent to obtain it. He had no difficulty in persuading the Amazon queen to part with the belt but Hera, angry at the ease with which the assignment was completed, disguised herself and told the wild race of women that Heracles was abducting their queen. He was lucky to escape the area with his life intact.

Geryon was a monster who ruled the island of Erytheia. He had three heads and owned a herd of cattle which Heracles was ordered to bring to king Eurystheus. Helios, the Sun god, lent Heracles a great golden goblet in which the Hero sailed to the island. The cattle were guarded by Orthros, the two-headed hound, which Heracles clubbed to death before killing Geryon himself and taking the herd. On his journey home, the prize bull broke away from the rest of the cattle and got mixed with the herd of King Eryx, who challenged Heracles to a wrestling match when he demanded the return of the animal. The superior strength of Heracles won the day, he re-captured the bull and brought the whole herd safely to Tiryns.

Heracles had to travel far and wide to fulfil his next task, the bringing of the Golden Apples from the garden of the Hesperides, to the king. After many adventures, Heracles reached the garden where he found Atlas supporting the sky. Atlas offered to get the apples if Heracles would hold the firmament while he went. Heracles shouldered the burden unsuspectingly, but when Atlas returned, saying that rather than take the sky back, he would take the apples to Tiryns himself, Heracles at last showed a bit of sense and agreed, but asked Atlas to take the sky for a moment while he put something on his shoulders to ease the pressure. Atlas took the weight and Heracles left with the apples.

Eurystheus sent Heracles to Hades. The last assignment was to bring back Cerberus, the mighty three headed dog which guarded hell. The god of the Underworld gave Heracles permission to take the dog as long as he used no weapons, only his bare hands. The great Heracles overcame the monster and took it back to the upper world and to Tiryns but Eurystheus did not really want such a fearsome monster and Heracles had to take it back.

His labours completed and back in Tiryns, Heracles fell in love with Iole, a king's daughter from Oechalia, but her father and brothers would not let her leave the family home. One brother, Iphitus, went to Tiryns in search of some lost cattle, although it is said that perhaps Heracles had stolen them. There our hero threw Iphitus to his death from the city walls. Once more repentant, and perhaps Hera had been responsible for his action, Heracles begged the Delphic Oracle for advice, for he was again afflicted with bouts of terrible madness, a punishment from the gods for his latest deed.

The priestess at Delphi refused to pronounce the Oracle for Heracles and in his fury he snatched the sacred tripod away. Apollo fought him for it and Zeus himself had to intervene, sending a thunderbolt to separate the two. The Pythia then told Heracles that he would have to serve a period of three years as a slave of Omphale, queen of Lydia, for whom Heracles performed many courageous deeds during his time of slavery.

A certain Lydian farmer, Lityertes, treated passers-by in a fearful manner. He invited them into his home, wined and dined them and then insisted that they take part in a contest. They had to harvest his wheat alongside him, whipped into competing with him for speed and production. This brute of a man always won, when he would cut off the heads of his competitors.

Now it happened that a shepherd, by the name of Daphnis, was searching for his lost girl friend, Pimplea, whom, he had been informed, had been sold to the Lydians as a slave. His search took him near Lityertes' land and he was ordered to compete in the reaping of the harvest. But Heracles took his place, working faster than Lityertes, whose head he cut off with his scythe. The land was rid of a tyrant, Daphnis was re-united with his Pimplea and Heracles presented the couple with Lityertes' fields, as a wedding gift.

You will have read in part one that while Heracles was serving the queen of Lydia he captured the two Cercopes, two mischeivous men who cheated, stole and generally annoyed everyone. Then Heracles killed a fierce dragon which was destroying Lydia's crops and eating humans and Omphale, by whom the hero had begotten several children, released him, in gratitude, from the slavery ordered by the Oracle and

87

Heracles returned to Tiryns, cured of his affliction.

When death was near, Heracles had one of his sons build a funeral pyre on Mount Oeta. Heracles climbed on and ordered his son to light it, but the boy could not bring himself to obey. A passing shepherd, Philoctetes, agreed to perform the act in exchange for Heracle' arrows. When the flames died down, nothing could be found of the hero's remains. It is said that he found the immortality promised by the Oracle, took his place among the gods on Olympus and married Hebe, the goddess of Beauty and Youth.

THE ORACLE SPEAKS TO THE CHILDREN OF HERACLES

By the time Heracles died, King Eurystheus had become a very powerful king of both Mycenae and Troezen, in the Peloponnese. Worried that as soon as they reached manhood, the children of Heracles would seek revenge for the way he had treated their father, he banished them from the land. They were given refuge in Athens by the king, Theseus.

Eurystheus demanded that they be given up to him but Theseus refused and as a result the two kings met in battle at Marathon. The Oracle warned that unless a noble woman was given in

Hyllos goes to Delphi

sacrifice, the Athenians would lose the fight. Makaria, Heracles' daughter, offered herself up and Theseus routed the opposition, winning the day. Some say that Eurystheus was killed in the skirmish and others say that he was taken prisoner to Alcmene, mother of Heracles, who had him put to death.

When the eldest son of Heracles, Hyllos, was old enough, he travelled to Delphi to ask the Oracle how he could defeat Atreus, who had succeeded to the throne of Mycenae on the death of Eurystheus, the throne which the boy felt was rightly his.

The Oracle told him that he should 'wait for the third fruit'. Hyllos assumed that 'fruit' meant the harvest and attacked the Peloponnese, at the head of an Athenian army, after three years had passed. He failed to hold the country however, when a plague broke out and the Delphic Oracle, when consulted, told him that he had invaded too soon. He withdrew his forces and waited for another three years. He then attacked again, meeting the opposing army at the Gulf of Corinth. Hyllos

suggested to their leader that the matter be settled by a duel between himself and any champion they cared to pick. If he, Hyllos, lost, then no attempt would be made to take the Peloponnese for one hundred years. The Peloponnesians chose Echemos of Arcadia to represent them and Hyllos was killed in the ensuing fight. As had been agreed, the Athenian army retreated and peace existed between the two kingdoms.

Many years later, Temenus, the grandson of Hyllos, approached the Oracle once more, to ask how he could win the Peloponnese. The priestess gave him the same message as before, but Temenus asked for an explanation. He was told that the third fruit did not mean the third harvest, but the third generation. The Oracle suggested that when he tried to take the peninsula, the attack should be led by 'a three eyed one'.

Temenus and his army, on the way to battle, met a certain Oxylos, who was riding on a one-eyed donkey. They crossed into the Peloponnese under the leadership of Oxylos on his donkey and were successful, defeating the enemy troops who were led by the son of Orestes, whom we shall meet later, and the land was divided between the descendants of Heracles.

THE ORACLE PLAYS A PART IN THE QUEST FOR THE GOLDEN FLEECE

A cerain King Athamas put aside his wife, Nephele, and took another. His new wife, Ino, wished to be rid of Nephele's children, namely a boy, Phrixus and a girl, Helle. She made sure that the crops failed, so that Athamas sent a man to consult the Delphic Oracle. Ino intercepted the messenger on his return and bribed him to tell the king that he must sacrifice his son, Phrixus, to avoid famine. The unhappy king was preparing to obey what he thought was Apollo's command and sacrifice his son when a fabulous winged ram appeared, its fleece shining gold. Phrixus and his sister Helle climbed on its back and it flew away. Helle fell off and into the sea which is now called the Hellespont, but Phrixus flew on

and landed in Colchis, near the Black Sea. There he sacrificed the ram to Zeus in thanksgiving and presented the Golden Fleece to the king, Aetes, who had it nailed to a tree in a sacred grove, guarded by a fierce dragon. Phrixus married a daughter of Aetes, lived to a good age and was buried in Colchis. The Colchians were a war-like people and the capture of the valuable and envied Fleece presented a great and seemingly insurmountable challenge.

A man named Pelias had forcibly taken the kingdom of Thessaly which rightly belonged to his half brother, Aeson, a nephew of Phrixus. When Aeson's wife bore a son, who was the rightful heir to the throne, the couple announced that he was dead, sending him to be brought up in secret on mount Pelion by Cheiron the Centaur, half man, half horse. Cheiron named the boy Jason. Pelias, meanwhile, had been warned by the Oracle at Delphi that his death would be caused by a relation, a man with one sandal.

When Jason reached adulthood and learned of his birthright, he made his way to Iolcus, where

Pelias ruled, to claim the throne. On his way he helped an old woman to cross a stream, losing his sandal in the swift running water as he did so. He did not know that he had carried the goddess Hera on his shoulders. She had wanted to test the young man as she had plans to use him, in a roundabout way, to overthrow Pelias.

When the king was told that a man with one sandal had arrived in the city, he hurried, fearfully, to meet him, demanding to know his name. Jason told him, and said that he had come to claim his kingdom. Now the god Zeus demanded that certain laws of hospitality be obeyed, so the king did not feel free to kill Jason. One legend says that Pelias asked Jason what he himself would do if the Oracle had said that someone would kill him, and Jason replied that he would send him to bring the Golden Fleece. Another tale tells that Pelias said he would give up the kingdom willingly if Jason brought back the Golden Fleece so that, according to a wish expressed by the Delphic Oracle, the spirit of Phixus could be at peace. One way or another, Jason agreed to go on the quest for the Fleece and Pelias assumed that he would never

Two bronze tripods

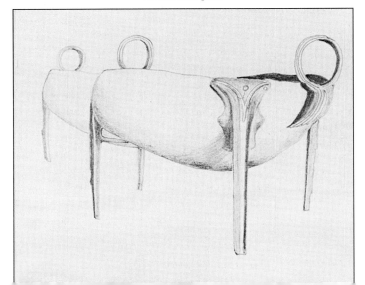

return.

The young Jason set about his preparations eagerly and with a spirit of adventure. He first took advice from the Oracle at Delphi, where the Priestess gave him two huge bronze tripods. Then he issued invitations to noble young men of Greece to take part in the quest. He employed a boat builder, Argus, to build a suitable craft. The goddess Athena gave him a marvellous talking beam for the prow. The boat was called the Argo and its crew were known as the Argonauts, one of the strongest on board being Heracles, who took time off from his labours to join the quest for a short time.

After many adventures and escapades, Jason and his Argonauts succeeded in capturing the Golden Fleece. They could not have done it without the help of Medea, the enchantress daughter of the king of Colchis. The goddess Hera caused her to fall deeply in love with Jason and she boarded the Argo with him as he and his crew set out on the return journey to Iolcus.

The way back was fraught with danger, but the Argonauts were not far from home when they found themselves at the mercy of a fierce north wind and were washed ashore by a huge wave. They were thrown well inland into the heart of the Libyan desert. On the advice of a local goddess, Jason and his crew started to manhandle their boat to an inland lake, but in the desert heat they were driven to despair by their terrible thirst. It is said that at this point, Heracles, on his way to the Garden of the Hesperides to perform one of his labours, helped them by conjuring up a spring of fresh water.

Once they launched the Argo on the lake, the men could not find their way to the open sea. Now they made use of the two great tripods which the priestess had given them at Delphi before they set out on their adventures, offering them to the gods. In return, Triton, the Trumpeter of the Sea, appeared to them. After some persuasion by the men, the god pulled the Argo as far as the Mediterranean. The Argonauts were safely on their

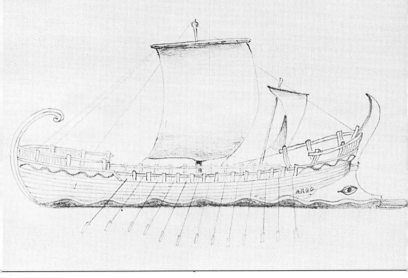

The Argo

way once more.

In Iolcus, Pelias was ageing. The voyage of the Argonauts had lasted many years and the king assumed that Jason and his crew had perished and the Oracle was thwarted. He killed Jason's father and considered himself safe but, with the help of Medea's magic, Jason got his revenge. The enchantress entered the city in disguise and told the king's daughters that she had the power to rejuvenate their father. She told them to cut an old ram into pieces and put the bits into a cauldron of boiling water. When they did so, she pulled a young lamb out of the pot. Impressed by this demonstration, the girls cut their father, Pelias, into pieces and put him into the pot. Of course, that was the end of the king. Jason and Medea were banished by Pelias' son and the Oracle was fulfilled, as Jason, through Medea, had been the cause of the death of Pelias.

Jason and Medea went to live in Corinth and had two sons. But Jason fell in love with Glauce, the daughter of the king of Corinth. He divorced Medea, threatened to banish her and made plans for his wedding. Medea reminded Jason of the times that she had helped him, but he told her that she should be grateful that he had brought her from wild Colchis to Greece, a civilised country. Medea, consumed with jealousy and a sense of injustice, left Corinth but sent her sons with a gift, in the form of a robe, for Glauce to wear on her wedding day. Glauce put it on, when it immediately burst into flames and she perished. Medea, knowing that her sons would be killed for the deed, murdered them herself. She fled to Athens, where King Aegeus gave her shelter and where we will meet her again. Jason died when, in despair and grief at the loss of Glauce and his children, he was sitting alone under the rotting hulk of the Argo and it toppled over, crushing him to death.

THE ORACLE AND THE HOUSE OF THEBES

Zeus fell in love again. This time it was with a mortal, a beautiful princess named Europa. In order to seduce her, the god took on the form of a handsome, gentle, white bull. He lay down before Europa, who climbed on his back, whereupon he leapt up and swam with her to Crete. There she bore the god two sons, Minos and Rhadamanthus.

Europa's brothers, meanwhile, went in search of her, told by their father not to return without her. One brother, Cadmus, not sure of where to start his search, went instead to ask the advice of the Oracle at Delphi.

Apollo told him not to look for Europa, but to find a cow with the markings of the full moon. He was to follow it and wherever it lay to rest, he was to build a city.

Cadmus found the cow, following it until it sank exhausted to the ground. Before obeying the instructions of the Oracle and building the city, which would become known as Thebes, he wished to make a sacrifice of the cow to Athena. Going to a nearby spring for water, he found it guarded by a huge serpent, which he killed. The spring was the Spring of Ares, and the serpent was a creature sacred to that god. Ares

Cadmus kills the serpent

demanded retribution and Cadmus had to serve him for eight years.

Cadmus became King of Thebes and married a girl called Harmonia. The gods attended their wedding and presented Harmonia with a wonderful robe and a magic necklace. The couple had four daughters and a son, but perhaps the god Ares never quite forgave Cadmus for

the killing of the sacred serpent, for there was a curse on the House of Thebes. Some of the descendants of the king suffered horribly and the Delphic Oracle played its part in the scenario.

Autonoe, daughter of Cadmus, married and bore a son, Actaeon, who, if you remember, was out hunting one day and saw the goddess Artemis naked, about to bathe. In her fury at being seen, she changed him into a stag and his own dogs tore him to pieces.

Cadmus and Harmonia had another daughter, Agave, whose sister Semele became mother of the god of Wine, Dionysus. Agave became a member of the god's cult of women followers, the Bacchantes. These women became frenzied with wine at the ceremonies of Dionysus and would tear animals or even humans to pieces in wild ecstasy. Agave herself became the mother of Pentheus, to whom his grandfather, Cadmus, handed the throne of Thebes. Dionysus, wishing to establish his worship in Thebes, came to that city followed by a group of frenzied women and Pentheus,

95

The god Apollo

King of Thebes, ordered the god to be put in prison, unaware that he was his cousin. The angry Dionysus made all the women mad, Agave included, who, not knowing what she was doing, was the first to set upon her son Pentheus, as they tore him to pieces.

The throne passed to Polydorus, uncle of Pentheus and only son of Cadmus. He married and had a son, Labdacus, but his rule was brief. He died young, leaving his wife as regent until his son could take the throne. But Labdacus, when he became king, also ruled only briefly. Some say that he was torn to pieces, like his cousin, for opposing the worship of Dionysus. His brother Lycus acted as regent until Laius, his only son, took the throne.

King Laius married Jocasta, a cousin, and when they had not produced an heir to the throne, he went to Delphi to seek the advice of the Oracle. It was not so much advice that he received as a warning from Apollo himself. He was told that on no account was he to have a child, because he was destined to die at the hands of his son.

Fate had decreed it, Apollo had spoken, but Laius thought that he could cheat destiny by refusing to lie with his wife. One night however, having had his fill of wine, he forgot himself and slept with Jocasta. The result was a son. The frightened Laius tied the baby's feet together, pierced them with a sharp instrument and left the boy on a mountain to die.

Laius ruled Thebes for many years until he heard rumours that the Oracle was about to be fulfilled. He set out for Delphi to learn more. A stranger on the road refused to give way to the king's chariot and Laius struck out at him. The angry youth pulled the king from his chariot and killed him. Unknown to Laius, the stranger was his son.

OEDIPUS AND THE ORACLE

And so we continue the tragic story of the House of Thebes, which sprang from an Oracle given to Cadmus by Apollo at Delphi.

The baby son of Laius, as you will have realised, had not died on the mountain where the king left him. Shepherds found him and took him to Polybus, the king of Corinth, who brought him up as his own son. He was named Oedipus, which means 'swollen foot'.

One day, Oedipus, teased for being a bastard, was so upset by the taunts that he travelled to Delphi to ask the Oracle if they were true. There he learned that he would kill his father and marry his mother. Once again, a man thought that he could escape his destiny. Oedipus, horrified at the prophecy of the Oracle, resolved never to go back to Corinth, thinking that he could avoid meeting his parents again. Not long after leaving the Sanctuary, Oedipus met a charioteer who refused to make way for him. We have heard how the impulsive youth pulled Laius from his chariot and killed him, unaware that the man was his father. Continuing on his way, Oedipus journeyed far and wide, arriving eventually at the city of Thebes.

In the absence of the king, the city was in turmoil. A winged monster with the face of a woman and the body of a lion, known as the Sphinx, was asking a riddle of anyone who entered the city, eating those who could not solve it.

The terrified Thebans, unable to answer the puzzle, had closed the gates to the city, leaving the Sphinx outside, and were in danger of famine. When, to add to their problems, a messenger had arrived with news of the death of King Laius, Creon, the king's brother-in-law, offered the kingdom and the hand of his sister, Jocasta, widow of the king, to anyone who could solve the riddle.

The newly arrive Oedipus heard of the reward and, as you will have read in part one, solved the riddle, when the angry Sphinx threw herself over the city walls to her death and Oedipus, in his innocence, took the prize and married his true mother, Jocasta. For a while, the couple ruled in peace and had two sons and two daughters. Then a plague ravaged the area and King Oedipus turned to the Oracle at Delphi for help. He learned that the plague would end when the murderer of Laius had been found and banished from the land.

Determined to trace the killer, Oedipus began investigating and finally discovered the two dreadful crimes that he had inadvertently committed. In her shame, Jocasta hung herself and the horrified Oedipus tore out his own eyes in despair. He left the area, accompanied by one of his daughters, Antigone. He went to Colonus, in Attica, where, we are told, he was protected by Theseus until he died. His two sons killed each other when arguing over the crown and one story says that his two daughters were condemned to death for burying a brother against the wishes of the Senate of Thebes.

THE ORACLE SPEAKS TO AEGEUS, KING OF ATHENS, WHO BEGETS A SON

Aegeus, king of Athens, had no children and was desperate for an heir. He journeyed, like so many before him, to Delphi, to seek the advice of the Oracle, where he was given a strange message by the priestess. Once again, it was more of a warning than an instruction. He was told not to loosen the mouth of his wineskin until he reached Athens. Puzzled by the words of the Pythia, Aegus set out for Athens by way of Troezen, where he consulted his learned friend Pittheus. Now Pittheus understood the Oracle, but decided to turn it to his own account. He plied Aegeus with wine before putting his royal friend to lie, in a drunken stupor, with his unmarried daughter, Aethra.

The next morning Aegeus, recovered from the shock of finding himself in bed with his friend's daughter, set out once more for Athens, but first hid his sandals and sword under a great rock. He told Aethra that if a son should be born from the night's lovemaking, and he was strong enough to lift the rock and take the weapon and sandals, then she must send him to Athens, where he would be recognised as the heir to the throne.

Some months later Aethra gave birth to a boy, Theseus, who grew tall and strong. When he was sixteen, his mother took him to the rock which he lifted with ease, finding the sword and sandals beneath. Aethra told him the story of his birth and Theseus set out for Athens to meet his father.

The boy had many adventures on his journey overland from Troezen to Athens, overcoming robbers and thieves who had plagued the people with their evil ways for many years. Fame for his courageous deeds spread before him. By the time he arrived, a great feast had been prepared for him in the city.

King Aegeus, however, had given shelter to the enchantress, Medea, after she had slain the wife and children of Jason. She realised who Theseus was and became jealous. She told Aegeus that the boy was dangerous and persuaded the king to put poison into his wine. Luckily, as Theseus drew his sword to cut some meat before drinking, the king noticed the weapon, recognised it as his own and dashed the cup from the boy's hand. Medea was banished for her deed and Theseus took his rightful place as heir to the throne, becoming especially popular when he killed a wild bull which was devastating the area around Marathon, causing dismay to the local people. It was the bull which Heracles had freed after bringing it alive from Crete to Tiryns.

It so happened that King Aegeus had once asked the young son of King Minos of Crete to try and kill the bull of Marathon, but unfortunately the boy had been mortally wounded by the animal. King Minos blamed Aegeus for the death of his son and demanded, in recompense, that seven maidens and seven youths of Athens should be sent to Crete each seventh year, where they were devoured by the Minotaur, that monster, half human, half bull, which was kept in a labyrinth on the island. Theseus offered to go as one of the youths

who, together with the girls, always sailed to Crete in a black-sailed ship. Of course, before setting out, he made the journey to Delphi in order to ask Apollo for guidance.

Through the Oracle, the god told him to take Aphrodite, the goddess of Love with him. She must indeed have accompanied him for, when he arrived in Crete, King Minos' daughter, the lovely Ariadne, immediately fell in love with the young man. She said she would help Theseus find his way in and out of the labyrinth if he would take her to Athens as his wife. This Theseus promised and Ariadne gave him a magic ball of thread which would guide him to the Minotaur. Theseus thus found his way to the very centre of the labyrinth where he and the monster met and, after a long struggle, the beast was killed. With the help of the magic thread, the hero escaped from the complicated maze of passages and set sail for Athens with Ariadne.

Some say that he left Ariadne asleep on Naxos, others say that Dionysus, God of Wine,

The black sailed ship

kidnapped her and other tales tell that Theseus fell in love with someone else and deserted her, but Ariadne never reached Athens. Still more tragic, Theseus had told his father Aegeus that should he be successful in killing the Minotaur, he would put up white sails on his ship instead of the usual black, but he forgot to do so. King Aegeus, watching for the vessel, saw the black sails and in his grief, thinking that his son was dead, drowned himself in the sea which after that was always known as the Aegean Sea.

If Aegeus had understood the meaning of the Oracle's warning, and not drunk wine before reaching Athens, Theseus might never have been born and Aegeus perhaps would have lived longer. But now Theseus became a great king of Athens and thereafter the stories of his exploits do not involve the Oracle and can be read about elsewhere, along with the tales of his courageous deeds on the way from Troezen to Athens as a young man.

THE CURSE OF THE HOUSE OF ATREUS

When Eurystheus, king of Mycenae, died, the people

consulted the Oracle to decide who should be king in his place. They were told to choose one of the two brothers who ruled Midea, Thyestes or Atreus. These brothers, like many the world over, were always in competition with each other. When the people found the choice difficult, Thyestes suggested that the throne should go to the brother who could produce a golden fleece.

Now it happened that Atreus had a gold sheep among his flock, so he agreed wholeheartedly to the idea. However he did not know that his faithless wife, Aerope, had given the fleece to her lover, Thyestes, who showed it to the people and was made king.

Atreus enlisted the help of the god Hermes, who told him to tell the people that the kingdom should go to a man who could reverse the course of the sun. Thyestes agreed, thinking that the task was impossible, but the gods of Olympus, to the astonishment of everyone, moved the sun backwards and Atreus took the throne.

Angry with his brother for stealing the fleece, Atreus banished Thyestes. Legend had it that before Thyestes left the kingdom, Atreus served him a meal and, when he had finished, told him that he had eaten his own sons. The horrified Thyestes pronounced a curse on Atreus and his seed.

The exiled Thyestes, wanting revenge for the horrible murder of his children, went to the Delphic Oracle where he was told to have a son by his own daughter. This son, the Oracle said, would wreak the revenge. Thyestes travelled to Sicyon, where his daughter, Pelopia, was a priestess. In disguise, Thyestes obeyed the Oracle and raped his daughter. Unknown to him, during the night Pelopia stole his sword and hid it in the temple where she served the goddess Athena. When Thyestes discovered his weapon to be missing, he left hurriedly, worried that the finder would discover his identity.

Atreus meanwhile had also consulted the Oracle. He was told to bring Thyestes back from Sicyon. So he set about doing as he was commanded, but arrived in Sicyon too late. He had just missed his brother and was not able to obey the instruction. But he met and fell in love with Pelopia and married her. When Pelopia had Thyestes' son, she left it on a mountain to die, but the child was found by goatherds, who cared for it, giving it to a goat for suckling. They named the boy Aegisthus, after the Greek for a he-goat and eventually they took the child to Atreus, who raised it as his own. Some say that he already thought that the child was his and that Pelopia had tried to kill it in a moment of madness.

Some years later, Atreus was back in Mycenae, where the land was suffering badly from a drought. He sent his sons by his first wife, namely Agamemnon and Menelaus, to Delphi, to ask if the whereabouts of Thyestes was known, bearing in mind that he had failed to carry out the earlier instructions of the Oracle. The two boys met Thyestes on the road and persuaded him to return with them to Mycenae. Atreus at once flung him into prison and ordered the young Aegisthus to kill him. THe boy entered the cell with his sword,

where he was overpowered by Thyestes, who recognised the weapon as his own. Thyestes ordered the boy to bring Pelopia, his mother, to the prison, where all was revealed. Pelopia, horrified to discover that her father was also the father of her son, killed herself and Aegisthus took his revenge, as the Oracle had forecast, putting Atreus to death. Thyestes ruled Mycenae for a while until his nephew, Agamemnon, took the throne from him.

Agamemnon became a very powerful ruler, married Clytaemnestra and they had three children; two girls, Electra and Iphigenia and a boy, Orestes. When the war with Troy started, he set sail for that city with a large fleet which met at Aulis, where the weather became so bad that the ships could not leave. A soothsayer told the commander, Agamemnon, that the goddess Artemis required the sacrifice of his daughter, Iphigenia, before they could sail. Agamemnon sent for his daughter, allowing his wife to think that he had found a husband for the girl. So

Iphigenia thought she was going to her wedding when she was taken and laid on the sacrificial altar. But after the sacrifice the weather became calm and the fleet sailed for Troy.

Agamemnon was gone for many years. During his absence Aegisthus took not only the throne of Mycneae but also Agamemnon's wife, Clytaemnestra. A look out was kept for Agamemnon returning from the Trojan War and when at last he was sighted, the two lovers were ready. They killed Agamemnon and his concubine, Cassandra. So Aegisthus continued his rule, which lasted for seven more years.

Agamemnon's son, Orestes, was sent by his sister, Electra, to a place of safety on the death of his father. When Orestes was old enough, he travelled to Delphi to ask the Oracle how he could avenge his father's death. He was ordered to kill both Aegisthus and Clytaemnestra and with Electra's help, he did so.

All was not well with Orestes. Even though the Oracle had ordered the killing, the Erinnyes, those whom the Romans called The Furies, punished Orestes by driving him mad. He went again to Delphi to ask how he might be cured. The Oracle ordered a year of exile for Orestes, after which he had to return to Athens, to be tried for the murder of his mother.

So Orestes wandered far, always tormented by the relentless Erinnyes, until it was time for him to return to Athens and stand trial. There Apollo defended him and the Erinnyes stood for the prosecution. Apollo's oration won the day. He stated that a mother was of no account; she was merely the vessel for her husband's seed and that Orestes had done no wrong. Athena's vote decided the verdict, Orestes was found not guilty and he returned to Mycenae, a free man.

But Orestes was not altogether free. Some of the Erinnyes continued to persecute him. So he went to the Oracle once more and, in the temple of Apollo, implored the god to help him. He was told to go to the land of the Taurians and bring to Athens a wooden statue of the goddess Artemis, which stood in the temple dedicated to her.

Now it so happens that when Iphigenia was lying on the sacrificial altar, before Agamemnon's fleet sailed for Troy, Artemis had saved her at the last moment, unknown to anyone, and transported her to the land of the Taurians, where she was made the Priestess of the temple of the goddess.

Orestes travelled to the land where the Taurians lived but, on landing and going ashore with his friend Pylades, the couple were captured by shepherds. They were taken to the king, Thoas, who ordered them to be taken to the temple and sacrificed. There, Orestes was re-united joyously with his sister, whom he had thought was dead. He told Iphigenia why he had come and they took the statue. However, the edict of the king still stood and Iphigenia devised a plan for their escape. She told the king that the two who had been sent to her for sacrifice were impure, as they had committed crimes. She was taking the statue of Artemis down to the sea to cleanse it in the waters and would take the two men as well. They had to be purified before Artemis would accept the sacrifice.

The king agreed and Orestes, Pylades and Iphigenia escaped to the ship together and aided, just as it seemed the king would stop them, by the goddess Athena herself.

And so at last Orestes was free from torment. The Erinnyes left him alone. He became King of Mycenae, eventually ruling over Argos and Sparta also, whose peoples regarded him highly. It is said that he died of a snake bite at the age of seventy. One legend has it that, years after his death, the Spartans were told by the Delphic Oracle that they would overcome the people of Tegea, with whom they were at war, if they brought the bones of Orestes to Sparta. The Oracle said they would find the remains in a place where two winds blew and '...where stroke rings upon stroke and where evil lies on evil.'

A certain Lichas, travelling in Tegea, stopped at a forge. He saw the smith hammering on an anvil while his assistant used bellows. He interpreted the wind from the bellows as the two winds, the blows of the hammer as the strokes and the anvil as the evil. When the smith also happened to say that he had found a coffin while digging on his land, Lichas persuaded him to part with it and took it to Sparta. The Spartans overcame Tegea. Due to the Oracle, Orestes' bones had found their resting place.

A DEATH IS ORDERED AT DELPHI

A Trojan seer named Helenus, captured by the Greeks, prophesied that Troy would not be taken unless the bones of Pelops were taken to that city and Philoctetes and a son of Achilles fought for Greece. So the bones of Pelops were delivered to Troy and Philoctetes, who, if you remember, was a shepherd who owned the arrows of Heracles, went to war along with a certain Neoptolemus, whose father, Achilles, had already been killed in the war.

Troy was sacked and Neoptolemus, who had fought very bravely, set out for home, where his first action was to go to Delphi to ask how he could revenge the death of his father. But it was Apollo himself who had killed Achilles in Troy and the Priestess refused to help. Neoptolemus burned down the shrine in his anger before leaving for Sparta, where he claimed Hermione for his wife, although she had been promised to Orestes. The marriage was not blessed with children and Neoptolemus, who ought not to have expected a good reception by the Priestess after his last actions, went to Delphi to consult the Oracle.

In a temple blackened by fire, he was told to sacrifice to the gods as a penance for his deed but, on approaching the altar, he found Orestes there. Orestes, burning with indignation at being deprived of Hermione, would have killed him at once but Apollo, knowing that Neoptolemus was going to die shortly anyway, stopped him.

As was the custom, the servants of the temple were removing the animals which had been sacrificed by Neoptolemus, taking them for food.

Neoptolemus tried to prevent this and the Priestess ordered his death. A dagger was drawn and the sentence carried out immediately. He was buried, by order of the Priestess, under the foundations of the new sanctuary. The ghost of the famous warrior, the servants of the temple were told, would guard it against all attack.

AUGE AND TELEPHUS

The Oracle spoke to Aleus, the king of Tegea. It warned him, in the usual devious way, that his wife's brother would be killed by her daughter's son. So Aleus immediately sent his daughter, Auge, to be a priestess in the temple of Athena, where he assumed that she would remain a virgin. One day, Heracles, on a visit to King Aleus, got drunk and going to the temple, lay with Auge.

When a famine came upon the land, Aleus was told that it was because the temple of Athena had been violated. Going to the shrine, he discovered that Auge was pregnant. The angry king instructed King Nauplion to drown her, but Nauplion decided to earn something out of the affair and set out for

107

A doe suckled Telephus

Nauplia, his kingdom, to sell her as a slave. On the way Auge realised that she was in labour and slipped away from the royal party. She gave birth to a son and left it to die, rejoining the king's entourage. In Nauplia she was sold to the king of Mysia, Teuthras, who fell in love with her and married her.

Meanwhile, Auge's son survived, suckled by a doe. Shepherds found him and named him Telephus, after the Greek word 'elapha', meaning doe. When the child reached manhood, he wished to know who his parents were and went, as was usual, to Delphi, to consult the Oracle. He received a simple message; he was to travel to Mysia. There he found his mother and married Argiope, the daughter of King Teuthras. One legend says that Telephus did indeed kill his mother's uncle and was struck dumb for doing so. His silence could not have lasted long, however, as he inherited the throne of Mysia and we have no stories of a silent king of that land.

In fact, when the Greek fleet sailed for Troy and war, it landed first in error at Mysia, where King Telephus was wounded by the sword of Achilles in the resulting battle. When the wound refused to heal, Telephus travelled to Delphi to ask the Oracle how he could be cured. The Oracle told him that only the one who had caused the injury could heal the festering sore.

So Telephus went in disguise to Mycenae, to the court of Agamemnon, where preparations were going on for a more successful expedition to Troy. There, on the advice of Clytemnaestra, he snatched the baby Orestes from his cot and threatened to kill him if he was not cured. It was quite an unnecessary action, for Agamemnon had been told that the assistance of Telephus was needed if the Greeks were to destroy Troy.

Agamemnon asked Achilles to heal Telephus but the hero retorted that he was no doctor; then Odysseus sugested that it was not Achilles, but his sword, that had caused the wound. Rust was wiped from the weapon and applied to the sore and it was healed as the Oracle had predicted.

Telephus guided the Greek fleet to Troy but would not take part in the war. After his death he was honoured as a hero.

A ROBE, A NECKLACE AND THE ORACLE

Oedipus, one time king of Thebes, had two sons, Polyneices and Eteocles, who agreed to share their father's throne turn and turn about. They quarrelled, as brothers will and, at the end of his turn, Eteocles refused to give up the throne. Polyneices went to Argos, where he sought the help of Adrastus, the king. There he married Adrastus' daughter and the king agreed to send an army against Thebes, enlisting the help of six of his chieftains. One of them, however, was a seer named Amphiaraus, who refused to go, predicting that the attack would fail and that Polyneices and the leaders of the expedition, with the exception of Adrastus, would die.

Now it so happened that the seer had a wife, Eriphyle, who always had the last word in any argument she had with her husband. Polyneices approached her and offered her the magic necklace which, if you remember, the gods gave to Harmonia, wife of Cadmus, years previously. He asked her, in return, to influence her husband in favour of the war. Eriphyle accepted the gift and told her husband to accompany the army to Thebes. Amphiaraus had to agree but, knowing that he was about to die, made his sons, Alcmaeon and Amphilocus, pledge to avenge his death. As he foresaw, Adrastus was the only leader left alive after the ensuing battle. The incident became known as the Seven against Thebes.

The sons of those who attacked Thebes wished to avenge the deaths of their fathers. The Delphic Oracle told them that they would be victorious as long as Alcmaeon, son of the seer Amphiaraus, led them. Alcmaeon was reluctant to go to war and it was Thersander, son of Polyneices, who repeated his father's trick and bribed Eriphyle, Alcmaeon's mother, this time with the robe which had been given to Harmonia at her

109

wedding feast. The greedy Eriphyle took the gift and persuaded Alcmaeon to attack Thebes.

The city was sacked and it is said that some of the spoils of war were given to Delphi. However, Alcmaeon discovered later that it was the greed and vanity of his mother that had led both his father and himself to war. He went to Delphi to consult the Oracle and was told to kill Eriphyle. He obeyed the Oracle and, as a result of his act of matricide, despite having been instructed to do the deed by the Oracle, the Erinnyes, the supernatural beings who wreak revenge on those who kill their relations, drove him mad. He wandered the land, in due time

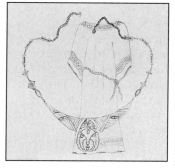

Harmonia's robe and necklace

arriving at a place called Psophis, where he married the king's daughter, Arsinoe, to whom he gave Harmonia's robe and necklace. When the Erinnyes continued to torment him and his wife bore him no children, he went again to Delphi. There, he was told to go to the river god, Achelous, who would purify him of the murder of his mother. Alcmaeon settled by the river, fell in love with Callirhoe, the daughter of the god and married her. Two boys were born to the couple, but Callirhoe heard about the fabulous robe and necklace of Harmonia and asked for them. Alcmaeon went back to Psophis and made up a story about the Oracle. He told the king that, in seeking a cure for his madness, he had been told that his affliction would only be cured if the robe and the necklace were presented to Delphi as gifts. The king however, learned the truth and ordered his sons to put Alcmaeon to death.

Callirhoe, hearing of the death of her husband, asked the gods to turn her children into men quickly. They grew overnight

Dionysus, god of wine

THE ORACLE AND A TERRIBLE SACRIFICE

In a place called Aroe, a boy and a girl fell in love. Their parents refused to allow the marriage so the couple stole away to make love in the sanctuary of Artemis. The angry goddess sent a plague to the area and the desperate people consulted the Oracle at Delphi. The priestess revealed the names of the lovers and commanded them to be sacrificed to Artemis. Not only that, each year the most beautiful girl and the most handsome boy were to be sacrificed to the goddess. The Oracle also predicted, however, that a foreign king, accompanied by a god, would arrive one day and put a stop to the terrible practices.

Now a certain King Eurypylos, sharing in the spoils of Troy at the end of the war, was given an exquisite chest which contained a statue of the god of Wine, Dionysus. Eurypylos opened the chest, saw the statue and was at once inflicted with fits of madness.

He set sail for Delphi to ask for a cure and there he was told that, when he reached a place where

111

and set out to avenge their father's death. When they succeeded in killing those responsible, they took Harmonia's robe and necklace to Delphi and left them there, where, it is said, pilgrims down the centuries were able to view them.

people offered strange sacrifices, if he settled there, his madness would leave him. Leaving the Sacred Precinct and returning to his ship, the wind came up and blew the vessel to Aroe where he landed in time to stop the sacrifice of a young girl and boy. Eurypylos showed the people the statue of Dionysus and they recalled the words of the Oracle. The king was cured of his madness and from that time on the dreadful human sacrifices to Artemis ceased and the people worshipped Dionysus.

POLYDORUS GOES TO DELPHI

Polydorus, the infant son of Hecabe and King Priam of Troy, was sent to Thrace for safety when war with Greece broke out. There he was brought up by his aunt and uncle,

Polymnestor dies

Iliona and Polymnester. They had a child of their own, a boy called Deiphilus and the two thought they were brothers.

When the Trojan war ended, King Priam was dead and Hecabe had been sold into slavery. Agamemnon felt threatened by the fact that a young prince of Troy still lived, thinking that one day the lad could stir up trouble for him. So he ordered Polymnester to put the boy to death. Polymnester however, had been charged by his brother with the boy's safety and in an agony of dilemma, he murdered his own son in the boy's place.

The result of this terrible deed was a rift between Polymnester and his wife Iliona. Polydorus, not knowing what had happened to his beloved brother but aware only of the increasing bitterness between his supposed parents, was deeply troubled and he went to ask the Oracle what the problem was.

The words of the Priestess were worrying. She

asked Polydorus why he had come to her with such a question, when his city was in ashes, his mother a slave and his father dead. The horrified boy rushed home, expecting to see the city razed to the ground and his parents missing, but instead he found that all was well. He sought out Iliona and told her of Apollo's grave mistake. So she told him the truth about his parentage, but when Polydorus realised that Polymnester had killed Deiphus, he took up his dagger and put him to death.

KING MINOS CONSULTS THE ORACLE

At the court of King Minos on Crete, the king's son, Glaucus, was playing. He chased a mouse and suddenly vanished. His worried parents searched everywhere but he was not to be found.

Of course King Minos turned to the Delphic Oracle for help. He was told that something very odd had occurred on Crete and the man who could find the most apt

Polyidus sees an owl

simile for the event, would find Glaucus.

King and courtiers made enquiries and discovered that a strange calf had been born which changed colour each day, from white to red and from red to black. All the wise men and women were summoned to the palace at Knossos but none could think of a good comparison.

Now it happened that a man from Argos was visiting the court in those days, named Polyidus, descendant of the most famous seer in all Greece, Melampus. He suggested that the calf was like a ripening mulberry and Minos joyfully told him to find Glaucus.

Polyidus was searching the palace, probably hoping for some inspiration, when he saw an owl by a cellar, surrounded by bees. The Greek word for owl is 'glaux' and it seemed to be an omen. Polyidus went into the cellar and found the child drowned in a great jar of honey. King Minos locked a protesting Polyidus into the tomb with Glaucus and ordered him to restore the child to life.

Entombed with the boy's body, Polyidus saw a serpent crawling towards him and, seizing his sword, killed it. A little while later he saw another serpent approaching with a leaf in its mouth which it applied to the body of its mate. The dead serpent came to life and crawled away. The astonished Polyidus took the leaf and placed it on the body of Glaucus. The young prince was resurrected and the grateful Minos showered Polyidus with gifts.

Polyidus wanted to sail for his home, Argos, but Minos ordered him to teach Glaucus his seer's art before he left. Polyidus had to obey but, as his ship was leaving Crete, he told the boy to spit into his mouth. This Glaucus did and immediately forgot all he had been taught.

THE FIRST WINE IN GREECE

Icarius, so the story goes, made the first wine in Greece, or was given wine as a gift from the god of Wine himself, Dionysus. Icarius tested it on a group of shepherds in the woods near Marathon. Not being used to such a drink, the shepherds got so drunk that they saw double and thought that Icarius had put a spell on them. In their fear they killed him and buried him under a pine tree before fleeing the country. They had been watched, though, by Icarius' dog, Maera. It left the woods and ran home, going to Icarius' daughter, Erigone, pulling at her skirts until she followed him.

The dog led her to the freshly dug grave under the pine and proceeded to dig up the body of its master. In her grief, Erigone hung herself from the tree, first praying to the gods that, until her father's death was avenged, the young girls of Athens would copy her act. So, after many maidens were found hanging from pine trees, the puzzled people of Athens consulted the Oracle at Delphi, which explained to them the circumstances of Erigone's death.

Now it happened that, some years before these events took place, a beautiful daughter of the king of the Lapiths and a Naiad, attracted the attention of the god Apollo. He carried her to a place in Libya and named it Cyrene, after her. Cyrene herself produced a son, Aristaeus, who was given the gift of prophecy by the Muses. When he was grown, he went to Delphi to speak with the Oracle. He was told to go to the island of Ceos, where he found the people suffering from a severe drought. He told them it was because the murderers of Icarius had fled there and were living among the people. When the shepherds had been found and put to death and sacrifice made to Zeus, the rain fell and praise and honour was heaped on Aristaeus.

The spate of suicides in Athens ended and a festival was inaugurated, to be celebrated

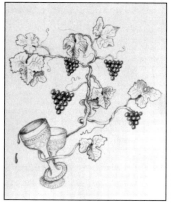

The first wine

115

down the years, in which wine was offered to the dead Icarius and his daughter and girls swung from pine trees in remembrance of Erigone's death. It is said that swings originated from this time.

THE ORACLE IS RESPONSIBLE FOR THE COLONISATION OF LIBYA

On the island of Thera lived Battus, a young man with a severe stutter, who travelled to Delphi to ask the Oracle how he could be cured. The priestess commanded him to found a colony in Libya but, as Battus could see no way to carry out the order, he returned home and did nothing.

Thera suffered a terrible drought

and the people sent to Delphi to ask what they had done wrong. The Oracle told them that Battus had ignored the command he had been given and suggested that they help him. So a party of Therans set sail but their guide landed, not on the mainland, but on an island just off the coast, called Platea. Several citizens were put ashore with provisions and the ship set sail for home, to find more settlers.

No-one, however, wanted to leave the beautiful island of Thera, and the drought continued. At last a reluctant Battus left with two ships, but he took one look at Libya and decided that it was not to his taste. He returned to Thera where the people, sick of the drought, forced him to turn

Battus sails at last

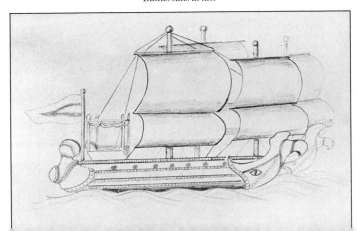

around and head back.

Battus and his party reached Platea and landed there but the colony did not thrive and the drought followed them. The Delphic Oracle reminded them that they had not colonised Libya, only an off shore island. Eventually Battus and his fellow colonists left Platea and settled in Libya as they had been ordered, so long ago. They made their home first on the coast at Aziris and finally at Cyrene, where rain fell in plenty and they prospered. Battus ruled as king.

One day, Battus was walking in the desert which surrounded his kingdom, when he was confronted by a lion. He screamed in terror, frightening the lion away and was cured forever of his stutter.

Battus is a historical, not a mythological figure, although these stories are legends which grew around his name. Cyrene was founded by Greeks in 633 BC and Pausanias describes a figure of Battus in his chariot, which stood at Delphi, sculpted by Amphion of Knossos around 400 BC.

THE ORACLE HELPS TO SHAPE HISTORY

The end of a Monarchy.

Kodros was the last king of Attica, in the 11th century BC. When the Peloponnesians decided to invade his lands, he of course consulted the Delphic Oracle. He was told that the side whose king fell, would be victorious. So he disguised himself and in rough peasant's clothes he picked a quarrel with some of the soldiers from the Peloponnesian army, who killed him in the resulting fight. When they discovered what had been done, the abashed Peloponnesians returned to their own land and Attica never had a king again; after this the rulers were called Archons. Some say this is legend, others put it in the realms of history.

The Olympic Games are Revived

In the 8th century BC, the king of Elis, Iphitos, asked the Delphic Oracle what he should do to save Greece, which was being ruined by civil wars. He was instructed to re-establish the Olympic Games. These games were very ancient and it is not known why they had ceased to be celebrated, but certainly from the time of Iphitos, who did as he was commanded, proper records were kept until the Games were abolished in 394. Iphitos also instituted the Sacred Truce, whereby all wars and fighting ceased for a period of three months while the Games were being celebrated. This enabled the athletes, judges and spectators to reach Olympia and return home again, unmolested. A heavy fine was levied on those who violated the truce and the Delphic Oracle would not speak to those who did not pay their fines.

SPARTA AND THE ORACLE

Lycurgus, who lived in the early 7th century BC, was responsible for laying down the laws which not only made Sparta a great military power but also gave its people a sense of community for the first time. Like most great figures, legends grew up around his name and the way he achieved fame. So the following story is a mixture of fact and myth.

When the Spartans were just a small tribe of people of no account, Lycurgus was a man

The Olympic Games are revived

who had been appointed guardian of their young king. Much loved by most of the people, his position still made him enemies; those jealous men who thought he wanted the throne for himself. Lycurgus left Sparta in disgust, travelling far and wide and learning much about the way in which different kingdoms were administered. Eventually, on his way back to Sparta, he visited Delphi, asking the Priestess if it was in his power to make good laws for his countrymen. The reply, from Apollo himself, was that his laws would be the best in the land.

On his return to Sparta, where news of the Oracle's reply to his question had spread, he was welcomed warmly. He set to putting his ideas into action and began to change the life of the Spartans, drastically. The land was divided equally among the people and plain living was decreed. Boys were taken at a young age, treated severely and taught to bear pain bravely. Girls were taught to wrestle and trained as athletes. The Spartan army grew in strength and fame.

When Lycurgus grew old, he set out for Delphi once more, but first asked the Spartans to keep his laws steadfastly until his return. This they promised and Lycurgus started for the Sanctuary. There, he asked Apollo his opinion on the laws he had made. The god answered that they were exellent and that the city that kept them would be most glorious. Lycurgus sent the words of the Oracle back to Sparta with a messenger but he himself did not return. His last request, before he died, was for his body to be buried at sea. That way, no one could say that he had returned home and the Spartan promise, to keep his laws until he did so, would hold.

SPARTA LOOKS TO THE WEST

The growing Spartan tribe cast an eye on Messenia, the land bordering them to the west. War broke out between the two peoples and at one point the desperate Messenians, hard pressed, sent a messenger to Delphi to ask for help from the Oracle. They were told that the people who first placed one hundred tripods on the altar dedicated to Zeus, at Ithome, would win the battle that was raging.

The Messenians immediately set to work. Trees were felled, craftsmen engaged and slowly, the wooden tripods began to mount in number. But the news of the Oracle's reply reached the ears of the Spartans, who decided that clay tripods were easier and quicker to make. So, while the Messenians were still busy, a Spartan crept by night into Ithome and placed one hundred clay tripods on the altar of Zeus.

Seeing the offerings there the next morning, the people of Messenia lost heart and Ithome fell easily to the Spartans. Legend has it that, some generations later, the descendants of the people of Ithome rose against their Spartan masters. So successful was the uprising that the Spartans were forced to consult the Oracle. They were told to ask Athens for a leader. Reluctantly the Spartans obeyed, putting the Athenians in a dilemma. They could not disobey the gods, but the last thing they wanted was a powerful Sparta. So they sent as a leader, thinking themselves very clever, a certain Tyrtaeus, a schoolmaster who was no warrior.

However, Tyraeus was a poet, who began to write stirring battle songs for his men. The Spartan army marched to war singing of courage and heroism. The powerful words of Tyraeus filled them with a conquering spirit which put fear into the hearts of their enemies, who scattered. The Spartans won their battles against the people of Ithome and grew ever more powerful.

A SPARTAN COLONY

Still in the 7th century, after Sparta had endured much internal strife, as developing nations do, those citizens suspected of plotting against the state were sent to Italy to found a colony at Tarentum. Phalanthos, the leader of the group, was told by the Oracle at Delphi that, as soon as he felt rain coming from a clear sky, he was to take the town.

Unfortunately, he did not have the Oracle explained to him and it was only after he landed in Italy and failed to take possession of any town that he suddenly realised that rain could never fall from a clear sky.

Very depressed, Phalanthus sought the comfort of his wife, Aithra. He put his head in her lap and she, feeling sorry for him, began to cry. Phalanthus felt her tears and at once understood the meaning of the prophecy. Today the Greek word 'aithria' still means 'clear sky' and his wife's tears were the rain The next day, Phalanthus took the great city of Tarentum with ease.

PERSIA SPREADS ITS EMPIRE

Croesus was the last king of Lydia who, in the mid 6th century BC, amassed a great fortune for which he became famous, along with the richness and piety of his gold offerings to Apollo at Delphi. He wanted to extend his borders and on consulting the Oracle, he was told that if he crossed into Persia, a mighty empire would fall.

As usual, the prophecy was ambiguous. Croesus took it to mean that the Persian empire would fall to him. So he went to war. But it was the fall of his own kingdom that had been predicted and Croesus perished under the might of the Persian army, although at Delphi it was said that, during the battle, he was miraculously saved and a poem tells of him being carried by Apollo to the land of the north wind.

THE ORACLE IS BRIBED

The Peisistratids, a tribe who ruled Athens in the 6th century BC, banished a powerful family, the Alkmaeonids, from the city. They fled to Delphi where they had kinsmen and when, in 548 Bc, the temple of Apollo was destroyed by fire, they undertook the re-building work, headed by Kleisthenes. There, it is said, they used their resulting influence and prestige to bribe the priestess when she was consulted by Sparta. She ordered the Spartans to liberate Athens from the Peisistratids. Reluctantly the Spartan king, Kleomenes, attacked and won the day. So Kleisthenes and his family returned to Athens to rule, but other powerful families gathered against the Alkmaeonids and the entire clan was exiled once more, only to return again later.

THE ORACLE AND A PERSIAN KING

In 483 Bc the Persian king, Xerxes, began the long preparation for invading Greece. He intended taking the entire country and to this end he built a canal at Athos for the passage of his fleet, and a bridge of boats which would enable his army to cross the Bosphorus.

In 480 Bc Xerxes marched from Sardis. The Spartans, when they had spoken with the Oracle at Delphi, learned that either Sparta or a Spartan king would fall. Athens also took advice from the Oracle and was told by a reluctant Priestess that a wooden wall would survive destruction and that divine Salamis would destroy the children of women. As usual the Oracle could be interpreted in different ways. The consensus of opinion in Athens was that the wooden walls were the fences that surrounded the upper city of Athens, but Themistokles, the leader of the Athenian Assembly at that time, who may well have had some influence on the pronouncement from Delphi, was of the opinion that the

Part of the Sanctuary of Athena Proinoa

wooden walls meant the Athenian fleet of wooden ships which he had been building fast, and that 'divine Salamis' meant victory at Salamis. Those who listened to Themistokles' version of the Oracle sent their families away to the Peloponnese, in particular to the town of Troezen, for safety.

Xerxes marched and at Thermopylai, Leonidas the Spartan king fell, together with 300 of his men, as they fought heroically defending the pass, but also fulfilling the Oracle given to the Spartans. Athens was evacuated in haste as Xerxes and his army drew near. The wooden walls of the upper city were burned and the Acropolis fell to the Persian forces.

In the narrow straits of Salamis, a great sea battle was fought, watched by Xerxes from the shore, where he sat on a golden throne. The Greeks won the day in their wooden ships, the Persian army was conquered and afterwards the Athenians showered Delphi with gifts in thanksgiving to Apollo.

Xerxes sent a detachment of soldiers to plunder the temple at Delphi. On reaching the Sanctuary of Athena Pronoia, or Athena the Protectress, thunder was heard and two great rocks rolled down the mountainside, crushing the soldiers to death.

THE GREAT KING PHILIP AND THE ORACLE

In the mid 4th century BC, Philip of Macedon dreamed that he had shut away the body of his wife, sealing the enclosure with a lion seal. Another time he had seen a serpent lying beside his sleeping wife. Perturbed by these things, he sent a messenger to Delphi, to ask the advice of Apollo. He was told to sacrifice to Ammon and to worship him above all other gods. Ammon was an Egyptian god and we do not know why Philip was ordered to pay him homage. We do know that Philip's son, Alexander, actually went to visit the oracle of that god, situated at an oasis in the Libyan desert. The Delphic Oracle also told Philip that one day he would lose the eye which had dared to see the god, disguised as a serpent, lying with his wife.

In 1977 AD, a Professor

123

Andronikos found two intact tombs behind ruins of other royal graves, at Vergina in northern Greece. It is thought that one of the tombs contained the remains of Philip of Macedon; the right eye appears to have been damaged by an arrow.

ALEXANDER CONSULTS THE ORACLE

Philip's son, Alexander, went to Delphi. He was about to embark on a war and wished to know the outcome. Unfortuately, he arrived at the Sanctuary on a day that the Priestess was forbidden to phrophesy. When she refused to deliver an Oracle to Alexander's messengers, he decided to go to the hallowed place himself. He pleaded with the holy woman in vain before he proceeded to drag her into the temple by force. Finally she turned to him and said,

'My son, you are invincible.'

Alexander immediately released the Priestess, having decided that she had told him all he wanted to know. And invincible he proved to be. We remember

him today as Alexander the Great.

DELPHI AND A SNOWSTORM

In 279 BC, Greece was attacked by the Gauls. The invading army, under the leadership of a man named Brennus, marched towards Delphi, knowing that the Sanctuary was rich in treasures, with the intention of looting it. In those days Delphi was protected by the Aetolians, who continually harassed Brennus and his men, slowing down their progress towards the holy place.

Now the Oracle had stated that Apollo would look after himself, aided by white maidens. So a startled army of Gauls, the legend goes, was suddenly confronted by the god himself, in the company of Neoptolemus and other heroes.

Battle commenced, lightning flashed and thunder roared. The terrified Gauls retreated to their camp where, during the night, a heavy frost caused great rock slides, further demoralising the hapless invaders.

The white maidens of Apollo appeared the next morning in the shape of snowflakes and, under cover of these, the Greeks conquered the Gallic army and Brennus committed suicide.

THE LAST ORACLE

In the year AD 267, the Heruli, a tribe of people from the north, passed through the Bosphorus and raided the Aegean, burning and plundering their way across the land. They destroyed Ephesus and much of Athens and perhaps it was this same tribe that sacked Delphi. With the spread of Christianity, Delphi did not recover. In AD 361 however, the Emperor Julian, nephew of Constantine the Great, ruled the land. His father had been killed by Christians so he had no cause to love them. When he came to the throne he attempted to restore the old gods. He sent his men to consult the Oracle at Delphi, which was spoken from the ruins by a priest.

"Say to the king," he said, "in ruin the once gay courts of the temple lie. Not a shelter of boughs has the god, nor speaks the laurel nor in the fountain. Silent is the voice of the water."

The Oracle never spoke again.

OTHER ORACLES FROM GREECE

Delphi was not the only place where oracles were given out, although it was the most important. Apollo not only prophecied at Delphi, but also at Gryneium and Clarus and there was a period in time when he found that no-one came to hear his advice in any of those places, for the head of Orpheus was speaking from a cave.

Orpheus, a wonderful musician, had, if you remember, descended into the Underworld to try and retrieve his wife. After that vain journey, he became a priest and worhipped Apollo, upsetting the god of wine, Dionysus. That god sent his followers, the Maenads, upon Orpheus and they tore him to pieces in a drunken frenzy. They threw his head in a river and it floated out to sea, some say still singing sweet music. The Muses buried his limbs and placed his head in a cave, where it prophesied and the people of the land came to consult his oracle

Magic, Monsters and Oracles from the Greek MythsORACLES

until the angry Apollos demanded that it cease.

Dodona, in Epirus, was the place of and ancient oracle of Zeus, his prophecies heard in the rustlings of oak leaves. That great god also had a famous oracle at Olympia, where after sacrifice had been made to the god, the priests inspected the entrails and t hen pronounced the oracle. Some of Apollo's oracles were pronounced in the same manner and Demeter's priestesses gave out her oracle, at Patrae, from the depths of a well. Tales of these other oracles occur in the Greek myths, but their origin is not given, although one could often hazard a guess.

ORION AND AN ORACLE

Orion was a hunter and a most handsome man who went to the island of Chios and there, as you will have read, he fell in love with Merope, daughter of Oenopion. When Orion asked for his daughter's hand, he was told to first hunt down all the wild animals that roamed the island. The task complete, Orion found that

Oenopion had no intention of giving away his daughter in marriage.

The hunter, inflamed with love, drank too much one night, entered Merope's room and lay with her. Oenopion called upon his father, Dionysus, for help and the god encouraged Orion to drink more wine until he fell into a deep sleep, whereupon Oenopion put out his eyes.

The blind Orion consulted an oracle, to be told that he must travel east and let the morning rays of Helius, the Sun god, fall on his eyes, when he would see again. Orion went eastwards in a boat to Lemnos, where he obeyed the oracle and recovered his sight.

AN ORACLE DEMANDS A SACRIFICE

Poseidon, like Zeus, had many love affairs. He seduced the lovely Chione and the girl bore a son, Eumolpus. Horrified at the result of the seduction, Chione threw the child into the sea, but Poseidon made sure that the baby reached Ethiopia safely. There, the child grew up and later married, but fell in love with his wife's sister and was banished from the kingdom. Arriving eventually at Eleusis, he became a priest of Demeter, celebrating her mysteries, even teaching the young Heracles. Eumolpus was famous for his piety and after some time became King of Thrace.

Athens and Eleusis went to war with each other and Eumolpus, heading a large force of Eleusians, claimed the throne of Attica. Erectheus, King of Athens, went to consult an oracle and was told that, if he wished to win the war, he had to sacrifice his youngest daughter to the goddess Athena. The king obeyed the oracle, whereupon his other daughters committed suicide. Erectheus killed Eumolpus in the ensuing battle before leading his troops to victory, thus fulfilling the oracle.

Poseidon, angry at the death of his son, asked Zeus to avenge the killing and Erectheus was struck by a thunderbolt.

AN ORACLE WARNS OF MASS MURDER

King Belus, a son of Poseidon, had twin sons, Aegyptus and Danus. Danus went to rule Libya and he begot fifty daughters called Danaids. Aegyptus ruled Arabia and had fifty sons.

When Belus died, the brothers fought and eventually Aegyptus suggested that, to make peace, his sons should marry the Danaids. Danus naturally consulted an oracle before making such an important decision and was told that his brother wished to kill all fifty girls.

Danus fled with his daughters to Argos, on the Peloponnese, where he was not only given sanctuary but, after some time, became king.

Aegyptus did not give up. He sent his sons to Argos, under orders not to return home until they had punished Danus. They planned to marry the Danaids and murder them on their wedding night. The people of Argos refused to allow them into their city; so they laid siege to it.

127

As there was no water in Argos at that time, Danus had to relent and he allowed the marriage of his daughters to the fifty sons of Aegyptus to take place. But he gave each of the Danaids a dagger to secrete into the bridal chamber. Only one of the girls did not murder her husband that night. Hypermnestra allowed Lynceus to flee, for he had been gentle with her. The girl was thrown into prison for her disobedience but eventually she and Lynceus were re-united and lived together happily at last.

THE GORDIAN KNOT

A poor peasant, Gordius, driving his ox cart one day, saw an eagle perch on it. The bird would not fly away, so the lad decided to drive his cart to Telmissus, where he had heard there was an oracle. As he approached the town, whose citizens were looking for a king, he was joined by a prophetess who had seen the eagle and knew its meaning. The pair entered the public square as the oracle was pronounced to the people. Their new king, it said, had just arrived on an ox cart.

So Gordius the peasant was proclaimed king as he tied his cart, with a peculiar knot, to the temple of Zeus. The oracle announced that the one who could untie the knot would become Lord of Asia. Many tried, but none succeeded, until an impatient Alexander the Great, also unable to undo it, cut the rope with his sword.

AN ORACLE AND PATRICIDE

Catreus was the son of King Minos of Crete. An oracle told him that he would one day be killed by one of his children. So two of them, his daughter Apemosyne and his son Althaemenes, left Crete hurriedly to try to prevent the prediction coming true. They made a home for themselves on the island of Rhodes, but one day Hermes seduced Apemosyne. When the girl told her brother what had happened he refused to believe her and put her to death.

Catreus, fearful of the oracle, banished his other two daughters and when he grew old, realising that he had no heir, he went to look for his son. He arrived, after a long search, at Rhodes, but when he landed on the island he was attacked by the local people who thought that he and his men were pirates. Althaemenes, hearing the noise of battle, joined in the fight, killing his father in the fray. When he realised what he had done and the oracle had been fulfilled, he prayed for death and his wish was granted by the gods.

ODYSSEUS GOES TO WAR

When Agamemnon prepared to set sail with his fleet to wage war on Troy, he wanted the hero Odysseus to join the expedition. Odysseus, however, had been warned by an oracle that if he went with the fleet, it would be twenty years before he returned home, a poor man. So when Agamemnon and his helpmate, Palamedes, arrived at the home of Odysseus to enlist him, he pretended to be mad. He was seen in the fields, ploughing, with an ass and an ox yoked together, throwing salt over his shoulder as he drove the odd pair. Palamedes snatched the hero's baby son and set him

down in the path of the plough. Odysseus at once brought the animals to a halt, showing that he was not mad and was persuaded to leave with the expedition. The oracle was fulfilled, for after the war with Troy, which lasted over nine years, Odysseus met with many problems on the return journey. He lost everything and twenty years passed before he reached home again.

THREE ORACLES AND THE TROJAN WAR

After nine years, the war against Troy was going badly for Agamemnon and his army. A seer said that only when someone armed with the arrows of Heracles fought on the Greek side, would they win and three oracles stated that Troy would not fall unless their conditions were met. Firstly, Pelop's shoulder blade had to be brought to the camp, secondly, Neoptolemus had to join the battle and thirdly, Athena's Palladium had to be stolen form the palace within the walls of Troy.

Now Pelops was the son of

Tantalus who, in his turn, was the son of Zeus. Tantalus, a mortal, was greatly honoured by the gods, for he was allowed to sit at table with them and share their food. The ungrateful man returned this hospitality in a dreadful way. He had Pelops killed, cut up and served to the gods as a meal. Only the goddess Demeter did not realise what had happened. She ate some of the hideous stew, including the boy's shoulder blade. The gods punished Tantalus severely. He was sent to Hades where he had to stand up to his neck in water. When he was thirsty and bent to drink, the pool would dry up instantly. Above his head hung a branch bearing luscious fruit, but it was just out of reach. He was tantalized.

The gods restored Pelops to life and Demeter had an ivory shoulder blade fashioned for him. He was a beautiful young man who eventually became king of Elis and the Peloponnese was named after him. When he died the people of Elis built a shrine for him at Olympia and it was there that Agamemnon's

man had to go, to fetch the ivory shoulder blade and take it back to the camp outside the walls of Troy.

Neoptolemus was the son of Lycomedes, king of the island of Scyros, and Odysseus was sent there, with Diomedes, to persuade Lycomedes to allow his young son to go into battle.

Philoctetes was the man who had lit the funeral pyre for Heracles, when he had been awarded the hero's bow and arrows. He had started out for Troy with the fleet but a snake had bitten him on the way. The wound had not healed and he had been left on the island of Lemnos. Odysseus and Diomedes, returning to Troy with the young Neoptolemus, stopped at Lemnos to ask Philoctetes to return with them. When Heracles appeared and assured him the wound would heal, Philoctetes agreed.

The Palladium was a sacred image of Athena and, back outside the walls of Troy, Diomedes climbed onto the back of Odysseus, got over the wall and managed to steal the figure. The conditions of the seer and all three oracles were fulfilled. The Greeks devised the Wooden Horse, filled it with their soldiers and wheeled it into the city, saying it was a gift to appease Athena, whose image had been stolen. At night, the soldiers crept out ot the horse, fired the walls of the city and Troy fell.

AN ORACLE AND A CHARIOT RACE

King Oenomaus of Arcadia had one child, a daugher, Hippodomeia by name and, some legends say, he was warned by an oracle that his son-in-law would kill him. To make sure that his daughter never married, he challenged all her suitors to a chariot race. Now Oenomaus loved horses. He owned two mares, sons of the wind, the fastest in the land. His wonderful chariot was driven by Myrtilus, the most famous charioteer in Arcadia and no-one had ever beaten his team.

One by one, Hippodomeia's admirers lost the challenge and were killed, until the handsome Pelops, son of Tantalus and friend of Poseidon, decided to take up the challenge. Poseidon gave Pelops a golden chariot pulled by winged horses and it is said that Pelops befriended Myrtilus, the king's charioteer, before the race and bribed him to loosen the wheels of the royal chariot. One way or another, Pelops won the race, killed Oemomaus, thus fulfilling the oracle and claiming Hippodomeia as his wife.

And so we come to the end of this account of Magical transformations, Monsters and Oracles. If the tales contradict each other at times, this is the way of myth, those stories passed down through the generations by word of mouth.

131

For those of you who visit Greece and wander through the countryside, will you take care where you tread, so as not to crush poor Menthe or Hyacinthus under foot? When you hear the shrill chirping of the cicadas, please spare a thought for the aged Tithonus and when you hear the sad tones of the nightingale, will you remember

Philomela and her terrible deed? If you are ever in the region of Mount Olympus and see its summit swirling in mist and cloud, you will believe that Zeus lives on. You will hear his voice in the rustle of oak leaves and know to take care not to anger him or any of his family, or you may take root in an olive grove or find yourself becoming some strange monster. No, be sure to please the gods of Greece and you wil live a long and happy life.

Index

133

137

Oxylos, 89

P